Soil Conservation Districts

in Action

Soil Conservation

The district program aims toward the goal of the complete farm conservation plan.

Districts

in Action

W. ROBERT PARKS

*Associate Professor of Government
and Agricultural Economics,
Iowa State College*

The Iowa State College Press • Ames

Library of Congress Catalog Number: Agr 52–461

To
Horace Parks

Preface

The soil conservation district is a unique administrative device. Created under state enabling legislation as legally independent units of local government, the districts have nonetheless had a close daily operational relationship with state and federal agencies, particularly with the federal Soil Conservation Service. Although the district is governed by a board of local farmer supervisors, responsible only to their local constituents, the board's policy decisions and administrative operations are conditioned in varying degrees by the professional agricultural workers assigned in the district's locality.

The soil conservation district, therefore, offers excellent opportunities for a case study of inter-governmental relations and of the problems and potentialities of lay farmer participation in agricultural administration. The first fifteen years of experience in the operation of the districts throughout the nation are the clinical materials out of which this study is made.

It is hoped that this study will prove useful to political scientists, agricultural economists, and professional workers in soil conservation, and also to the 12,000 farmer supervisors of the districts throughout the nation, whose day-to-day decisions are the most important determinant of the districts' success or failure.

Over a period of six years, the writer — first as a member of the staff of the Bureau of Agricultural Economics, and later of the Iowa State College — has studied the inner workings of the soil conservation districts. This has been through field study in a fourth of the states, and through examination of the various records and reports from districts in all of the states. The task has been made possible only by the splendid cooperation of many district supervisors, Soil Conservation Service and Extension employees in the states and counties, and many other people who have been closely connected with the district movement.

It is impossible in so short a space to thank individually the numerous people who have contributed so much toward making this study possible. Particular mention can be made of only a few who have contributed most.

Ellen Sorge Parks has done more than offer the sympathetic understanding customarily expected of a wife. She has been an invaluable associate in the making of this study. John M. Gaus, Professor of Political Science at Harvard University, did more than anyone else originally to direct my interest toward this type of research. Fred A. Clarenbach, Professor of Political Science at the University of Wisconsin — under whose direction the writer's Ph.D. disseration on soil conservation districts was written — has offered many valuable criticisms.

V. Webster Johnson, formerly Head of the Division of Land Economics of the Bureau of Agricultural Economics; Professor C. H. Matterson, Head of the Department of History and Government of Iowa State College; and Professor William G. Murray, Head of the Department of Economics and Sociology of Iowa State College, as thoughtful superiors have all given the writer encouragement.

Glenn E. Riddell and Wendell R. Tascher, who were Extension-SCS Conservationists during most of the period over which this study was made, deserve special thanks for their continuing interest and constructive criticisms. The writer is also grateful to T. L. Gaston, Alfred M. Hedge, R. W. Rogers, and Frank Mendell, all of the Soil Conservation Service, for their patience and cooperativeness in meeting the writer's almost constant requests for miscellaneous facts and figures.

It is, of course, understood that the writer alone is responsible for the nature of the treatment and the interpretation of the conclusions.

W. ROBERT PARKS

Ames, Iowa
July, 1952

Table of Contents

Illustrations

Soil Conservation Districts

in Action

CHAPTER 1

Beginnings of
the Soil Conservation District

After three centuries of exploiting a continent, the American people, in the sober mood of economic depression, awakened to the fact that they were rapidly losing their greatest resource, productive land. The dust storms, sweeping across the Great Plains, and the deepening chasm-like gullies of the Southeast were the dramatic manifestations of widespread destruction of soil resources through erosion and the mining of soil fertility.

By the 1930's, 50 million acres of once-good cropland were already destroyed, and another 50 million were badly damaged. Almost 75 per cent of all cropland was subject to soil erosion and therefore faced a similar fate. Soil productivity also was being lost through the leaching away of vast quantities of soluble minerals.

With the broad acceptance by Americans that they must act at once to preserve their soil came the questions: How was the job to be done? Who was to carry on so large an undertaking? Who was to bear its cost? Who was to give it guidance and direction? Who was to be held finally responsible for its accomplishment? Was the task to be left to the farmer alone? Or must responsibility be assigned to local, state, or federal government?

The stake which the farmer and each level of government had in preserving the productivity of the land gave each a responsibility in conservation. The farmer whose livelihood was being threatened by the destruction of his soil could not be freed from the obligation of conservation. Nor could the rural communities and counties, for their lives too depended upon the soil resources of their area. Productive soil was their governments' chief tax base. Their social and economic vigor was rooted in the prosperity of their farm people. State governments with

[1]

their responsibilities for the health and solvency of their communities likewise had a clear interest in soil conservation. The 1930's brought acknowledgment of a pressing national concern in the nation-wide protection of agricultural lands from impoverishment and ruin.

With the interest of farmers and all levels of government so identified with soil conservation, the question was which of them could do the job most effectively and economically. Clearly conservation could no longer be left entirely to the whim of the individual farmer. Governmental guidance, persuasion, and assistance were required. But could this persuasion, assistance, and guidance come from the local and state governments alone? Or was a national program also necessary?

DECISION FOR NATIONAL CONSERVATION PROGRAM

The New Deal Congress believed that only through a national program could the nation's soil resources be adequately protected with sufficient speed. National action was seen necessary, first because erosion problems, like so many of the newer problems of government, do not follow state boundaries. As H. H. Bennett observed:

> Erosion and its accompanying evils do not stop at fence lines, or farm boundaries. Neither do they stop at state lines. They are, in general, watershed or regional problems and must be treated on that basis. The Mississippi River, for example, in its long course touches and flows through three regions, while some of its tributaries — which make up its great watershed — find their sources in still three more regions. Obviously, this makes technical coordination imperative.[1]

The critical need for speed in saving the nation's soil was a second reason for national action. The requirement, it was originally estimated, was to get the basic conservation measures applied to the land within 20 years. Although many localities and states could be expected to go forward with conservation at a satisfactory rate, other states, it was felt, would loiter dangerously behind. If nation-wide soil conservation was to be accomplished with sufficient speed, there had to be a national force to press with equal emphasis in all communities, states, and regions for speedy local accomplishment.

National action was deemed necessary, in the third place, to

---

[1] *Report of the Chief of the Soil Conservation Service*, 1946, p. 4.

insure that uniformly high standards for conservation work were established and maintained throughout the United States.

Finally, soil conservation over a nation-wide area was thought to require material assistance from the federal government. What the respective contributions of the farmer, the local community, the state and the national government should in social justice be, has not yet been determined. As yet there is little agreement among those influencing agricultural policy upon the need or justifiability of benefit payments to achieve a conservation program. Nor is there common understanding of how much technical assistance, soil conservation equipment, and planting stock must be provided farmers by the federal government to insure satisfactory local soil conservation operations. As the House Committee on Long Range Agricultural Policy summarized:

> There has been a sharp difference of opinion as to where the major responsibility for soil conservation lies — with the farmer, local government, or the Federal Government. Some witnesses felt that the Federal Government should assume the entire responsibility through Federal conservation projects and payments to farmers. Others felt that the primary responsibility is on the farmer, who should know what is best for his land and will reap the profit from sound conservation practices and that this is the time for the Federal Government to stop paying the farmer to protect his own soil. Between these two extremes were varying opinions as to where the division of responsibility lies.[2]

For a variety of reasons, then, a federal agency, which became the Soil Conservation Service in 1935, was established and given the authority and responsibility to act to bring about desirable physical adjustments in land use with a view to bettering human welfare, conserving natural resources, establishing a permanent and balanced agriculture, and reducing the hazards of floods and siltation.[3] These broad objectives were to be achieved through several complementary programs: soil conservation, farm forestry, flood control, sub-marginal land utilization, and drainage and irrigation.

The central program of the Soil Conservation Service was that of conserving basic soil and water resources by extending sound land-use practices to all private land vulnerable to soil erosion and public lands, in cooperation with other agencies.[4]

---

[2] U. S. Congress. House Committee on Agriculture. Preliminary Report, *Long-Range Agricultural Policy*, 80th Cong., 1st Sess., 1947, pp. 9, 10.
[3] "Objectives and Basic Policies," *Soil Conservation Service Manual*, No. 11110, February 1, 1941, p. 1.
[4] *Ibid.*, p. 1.

Within the limits of its resources, the Soil Conservation Service was free to use whatever legal means it chose to carry out its responsibility in conservation.

The Soil Conservation Service first turned to nation-wide demonstrations of conservation farming in demonstration projects and CCC camp areas and on individual farms in cooperation with the state extension services. The purpose of the demonstration was to introduce conservation measures and practices applicable to a large natural land-use region by using a small watershed area that represented as nearly as possible a cross section of the region. However well such strategically scattered demonstrations pointed out the need, methods, and values of conservation farming, the demonstration program alone, it was felt, could not achieve nation-wide conservation farming. As an SCS administrator pointed out in 1937:

> From the standpoint of national adequacy, effective soil conservation requires the intensive and coordinate treatment of all lands in every natural region of similar soil, slope, climatic, and type of farming characteristics, in accordance with their needs and adaptabilities. This cannot be achieved, naturally, by the intensive application of conservation measures to the lands of a small group of farmers within boundaries of demonstration projects and camp areas.[5]

NEED FOR LOCAL GOVERNMENT IN CONSERVATION

Federal conservation administrators recognized that the federal government did not have the capacity to carry on single-handedly the job of getting adequate conservation measures applied upon each of the nation's millions of farms. Perhaps if unlimited federal material resources had been available, the federal government could have carried the work. But the thought was that nation-wide conservation could be accomplished more effectively, economically, and democratically, if local farmer government were brought into the conservation operation.

The Department of Agriculture had the difficult task of developing a national plan for conservation which would suit the ever-changing special needs and circumstances of thousands of local areas. The wide variations in topography, soil types, vegetation, climate, agricultural economy, and rural society present in so vast a land area, demand widely varying patterns of conservation measures. The Department saw local government

---

[5] Dillon S. Myer, "The Next Step: Emphasis Shifts to the Districts Plan," *Soil Conservation,* Vol. III, November 1937, p. 126.

as a means of tailoring a national conservation plan to the localities.

As the southeastern regional director of the Soil Conservation Service pointed out, a conservation program, national in concept and extent:

> . . . must be adapted to local conditions throughout the country. It must be fitted to the needs of the individual community. It is impossible for a central authority working alone to develop on a national scale a soil conservation program gauged and adapted to the needs of each problem area throughout the country. Neither can it be done on a regional basis. The state, even, is too large. It is necessary that consideration be given to the peculiar needs of each area appreciably different from other areas.[6]

The Land-Grant College Association's committee on postwar policy went even further in picturing the need for local adjustments in national agricultural programs:

> Instead of attempting to impose arbitrary national programs on localities — in effect demanding that all feet be fitted into the same size and style of shoe — we need, first of all, programs designed to fit states and counties. If the most feasible solutions call for action crossing state lines, then so far as possible they should represent a synthesis of state and local programs, the reverse of planning nationally and making adjustments locally.[7]

Although a national conservation program administered in the localities through a national bureaucracy might permit and encourage local variations to meet varying local circumstances, the probability of obtaining more genuine local adjustments is greater in an arrangement in which a local organization of citizens has an authoritative place in making local decisions. The Land-Grant College Association emphasized that:

> If the mechanism of planning and operating farm programs actually is to insure adaptability to local conditions, then far more responsibility and democratic opportunity for initiative and decision must be placed at the county level.[8]

The need for local government did not rest only in the fact that it made local adjustments in the national program more possible. The need was also for a local government which

---

[6] T. S. Buie, Regional Conservator, SCS, Spartanburg, South Carolina, Address Before Meeting of Service Personnel, Lexington, Kentucky, March 16, 1944, p. 4.

[7] *Postwar Agricultural Policy*, Report of the Committee on Postwar Agricultural Policy of the Association of Land-Grant Colleges and Universities, October 1944, p. 59.

[8] *Ibid.*, p. 61.

brought into local adjustment decisions the opinions and judgments of local farmers — farmers who had empirical knowledge of the needs and problems of their area and of local people's probable reactions to various proposals for conservation activity. The Department of Agriculture would have agreed with a later statement of the Land-Grant College Association that: "One of the most urgent needs of agriculture is a means of assuring that the programs and policies adopted actually are those which reflect the needs and wishes of local people." [9]

In the third place, local government was viewed as a vehicle for obtaining the positive farmer cooperation in conservation which is the basic essential in its successful accomplishment. The requirements in material resources and human labor for bringing under conservation 400 million acres of cropland and 600 million acres of other kinds of farm land were gigantic. Therefore, society, in undertaking soil conservation as a collective goal, had to require more of the farmer-citizen than the mere refraining from doing an illegal act. Rather, as in the achievement of so many of the new tasks for which society has made government responsible, the citizen had to share positively in the performance of soil conservation. The Soil Conservation Service has estimated that under the district program, the federal and state governments contribute about two dollars toward the conservation of each acre of farm land. At the same time the farmer must spend an additional three to five times as much in labor and material to conserve each acre of his land.

Even if it were publicly determined that the conservation of the nation's soil was of such critical national interest that the public generally should bear the total cost, the problem of governmental mobilization of the resources and labor for such an undertaking would be huge. Only in the depths of depression could public labor power be readily organized for carrying out conservation upon every farmer's land. The effect upon democratic society of such a mobilized corps of government labor in the carrying out, even with the farmer's passive consent, of such far-reaching governmental intervention into land-use can only be speculated. To achieve nation-wide soil conservation, the farmers of the nation must generally be so convinced of their need and their responsibility for playing an active part in the conservation program that they are agreeable to using chiefly

---

[9] *Ibid.*, p. 59.

their own labor and materials in putting conservation measures into effect upon their farms.

Placing the chief responsibility for the initiation and management of a soil conservation program upon local groups of farmers was seen as the most likely means of insuring farmer cooperation. In the first place, with the administration of soil conservation in the hands of local farmers, arrangements and processes in the conservation program can presumably be more nicely adjusted to the needs and reactions of the farm people of an area. Further, because their own neighbors have either determined or approved the conservation process, farmers are more likely to accept suggested conservation measures as necessary and practical. Moreover, centering responsibility for conservation upon local areas may make farmers, in their psychology, less dependent upon the material assistance of government in solving their agricultural problems.

Local democratic government was considered an end value in itself. It was the belief of the Wallace administration that local democratic farmer government was necessary to counterbalance the dangers to democracy arising from a centralized government's moving into a larger and more vital area of farmers' lives. In each of its action programs the Department sought to develop local arrangements which would permit great numbers of farmers to take direct part in determining and administering public agricultural policies within their own areas. Such local policy making and administration was also to influence national programming. In discussing departmental cooperation with soil conservation districts, Secretary Claude Wickard, in 1940, declared:

> The philosophy of democratic government revolves around the principle that the mass of people is capable of governing. It is my conviction that democracy, therefore, cannot be said to be succeeding unless the mass of the people participates in the affairs of government. Only their participation makes a democracy work.[10]

SELECTION OF SOIL CONSERVATION DISTRICT

Soil conservation was one of the new public tasks which did not well fit into old governmental molds. Seemingly no one level of government was equipped to do the job singlehandedly.

---

[10] "A Statement by the Secretary of Agriculture Concerning Departmental Cooperation with Soil Conservation Districts," *Soil Conservation Service Manual*, No. 49110, September 21, 1940, p. 1.

The need was for a type of intergovernmental mechanism in which the peculiar competencies, energies, and resources of each level could be pooled. A new working partnership was thought necessary which could merge in its operating process the values of both national and state programming and local democratic determination.

The concept of the conservation district grew out of these felt needs. In 1936 the federal government proposed the district to the states in a suggested "standard state soil conservation districts enabling law" which outlined district functions, powers, and organizational arrangements. Under federal leadership, the states and local people have turned to the soil conservation district.

Since 1937 all forty-eight states have passed legislation permitting the organization of districts. Over 2,400 districts have now been created. The Soil Conservation Service estimates that about six-sevenths of the districts necessary to cover the entire agricultural area of the United States have now been organized. These districts include more than 4,871,000 farms and ranches. Over 883,353,000 acres of land in farms and ranches are included within their boundaries. Approximately 77 per cent of the land in farms and over 83 per cent of the farms in the United States are now in districts. The districts, by January 1, 1952, had 920,361 active "basic" farm conservation plans which covered 256,532,447 acres.[11] Conservation measures have been applied to 150,066,359 of these acres.[12]

Some twelve thousand farmers are now acting as district supervisors — governors of their districts. In addition, the districts are employing an ever-growing number of clerical and sub-professional technical personnel. The capital resources of the districts which have been created through state and local efforts have likewise been growing. Supervisors themselves have increased their strength through their organization in forty eight state associations and the establishment of a national association.

Fifteen years of experience in conservation through district administration has now been accumulated. That the district is a flourishing, nation-wide, going concern, which will

---

[11] "Basic farm plan" is the term now used for the "complete farm plan," which, under the "progressive planning" procedure, adopted by SCS on April 9, 1951, is the final step in the conservation planning of the individual farm. See chapter 3.

[12] SCS, "Soil Conservation Districts: Status of Organization, by States, Approximate Acreage, and Farms in Organized Districts," January 1, 1952.

continue to grow in area, material resources, and strength, is generally accepted. The district has yet to be analyzed and appraised, however, as a governmental arrangement which took precedent over national, state, and county government as the agent for assisting farmers in getting conservation on the land. The critical question then is: Has the district so met the two large tests of effectiveness and democracy that its creation in addition to the traditional units of government has been justified? Does the district provide machinery for developing and carrying through an adequate conservation program? Is it bringing local democratic self-government into the conservation program?

Exploration of these large questions requires the investigation of a series of more specific problems: Has the district device created a suitable balance between national programming and local democratic determination? How much national direction must the district governments accept for the effective carrying out of conservation? What must the nature of the conservation program be if it is to be effective in achieving conservation? With what related agricultural problems which influence conservation accomplishment must an adequate conservation program be concerned? Should the amount of national direction and control in the conservation program vary with the nature and extent of the national assistance given to farmer cooperators?

Can district government be suitably geared into the new, integrated national "agricultural resources conservation program," in which the activities of the Soil Conservation Service and the soil conservation work of the Production and Marketing Administration are closely coordinated? Is there a possibility that the district may serve as a block in developing an integrated conservation program for each county? Or does the district have the potential for becoming the medium through which a total conservation program is brought to farmers? How will district relationships with cooperating and non-cooperating farmers need to be adjusted to gear in with the SCS technicians' new responsibility for providing technical assistance to Agricultural Conservation Payment program farmers? Does the newly integrated federal conservation program threaten the district's independence as a unit of local government?

To what extent have the supervisors exercised their governing powers in the determination and management of district activity? Has there been a productive blending in district administration of the experience and knowledge of supervisors with the specialized information of SCS technicians? What functions and responsibilities must the supervisors perform if they are in fact to govern their districts? What means are being used to increase supervisor management activity?

CHAPTER 2

Nature of the Soil Conservation District

After fifteen years of experience with the soil conservation district there is still disagreement on its governmental nature. The Soil Conservation Service has maintained that the district is an independent unit of local government. Others have viewed the district as little more than the local appendage of a federal agency. There is truth in both of these opposing contentions. However, arguments concerning the district as a unit of local government are relatively meaningless. The peculiar value of the district lies in the very fact that it is a hybrid in government. The test of its worth is its capacity to merge the best values of local government and national programming in its operation.

DISTRICT AS A LOCAL GOVERNMENT

Basic in the joining of the national conservation agency and the local conservation districts in a program of common action is the legal structural independence of both bodies. Each has the legal authority and power to carry on its own conservation program independently of the other agency.

The concept of the district as an instrument for conservation was first perceived by the federal government. District functions, powers, and organizational arrangements were outlined by the Department of Agriculture in a model act which was generally followed in state laws.[1] Finally, districts came into existence because of federal pressure upon the states to adopt the standard state enabling act and federal persuasion in the local areas to organize districts. Nevertheless, soil conservation districts are, in their legal structure and authority, local governmental subdivisions of the state, completely independent of the federal government.

---

[1] USDA, Soil Conservation Service, *A Standard State Soil Conservation Districts Law,* 1936. Hereafter, sometimes referred to as the "standard act."

Creation at Will of Local People

The establishment of a district is dependent alone upon the wishes of the farmers of the area and upon the decision of a state soil conservation committee. According to the standard act, districts can only be established by the following procedure: At least twenty-five land occupiers must first petition the state committee to establish a district. The committee is then required to hold a public hearing on the petition, to define the boundaries of the proposed district, and then to submit to all land occupiers living within the boundaries defined, the question of whether the district should be created. No district may be established unless a majority of the votes cast in the referendum are in favor of it.[2]

The states, almost unanimously, followed this principle that districts should be created only upon the wishes of local people.[3] Except in the seven states where the vote of local people is conclusive in making the decision to organize a district, a state body — the state soil conservation committee — makes the final determination for the organization of a district. In New York, Pennsylvania, and Wisconsin the final decision for creating a district is made by the governing body of the county. In Arizona,

---

[2] Citations for all state soil conservation districts laws may be found in Appendix A, Table 1. To avoid repetition, these citations will serve as the authority for all points of state law throughout this book, unless otherwise indicated.

[3] Nineteen states, following the standard act, provide that a district may be created in an area where 51 per cent of the votes cast in a referendum favor a district's establishment. These states are: Florida, Georgia, Illinois, Kentucky, Louisiana, Maine, Maryland, Michigan, Minnesota, Mississippi, Nevada, North Carolina, North Dakota, Oklahoma, Oregon, South Carolina, Tennessee, Utah, and Washington.

In California, Colorado, and Delaware a 51 per cent affirmative vote in a local referendum makes it mandatory on the state committee to establish a district. In New Jersey and Wyoming not only must 51 per cent of those voting in the referendum be in favor of a district, but the favorable votes must also represent a certain percentage of acreage in the area. Vermont requires a 51 per cent affirmative vote in a referendum, and further requires that a certain percentage of the eligible voters must participate in such a referendum.

Indiana and West Virginia require a 60 per cent majority. In addition, Indiana requires that a certain percentage of the eligible voters participate. Five states (Arizona, Iowa, Montana, Ohio, and Pennsylvania) require a majority of 65 per cent. Arizona also requires that a certain percentage of the eligible voters participate. Nine states (Alabama, Arkansas, Idaho, Kansas, Missouri, New Mexico, South Dakota, Texas, and Virginia) require a majority of 67 per cent. Nebraska requires the largest majority, 75 per cent.

In Rhode Island, the state committee is to decide if a substantial proportion of land occupiers favor the creation of a district. Because of the peculiar relationship of the districts to either the county or state government in Connecticut, Massachusetts, New Hampshire, New York, and Wisconsin, no local referendum is required in these states.

California, Colorado, and Delaware the decision made in the referendum is conclusive.

Legal Position of District

The legal definition of the districts clearly makes them subdivisions of the state, outside the legal reach of a federal agency. The state conservation laws usually follow the standard act in declaring the district to be either or both "a governmental subdivision of the State" and "a public body corporate and politic." Thirty-three states declare their districts to be both. New York and Wisconsin, because of their districts' peculiar relationship to the county, define a district as "a county whose board of supervisors has by resolution declared it to be a soil conservation district." Only six states (California, Connecticut, Massachusetts, Missouri, New Hampshire, and Ohio) failed to specify the governmental status of their districts. When the determination for organizing a district has been finally made, the district is then brought into existence through the regular channels for creating local governmental units.

Powers of District

Most important in establishing a district's legal independence is the authority which the states have given local districts to carry on those functions necessary for conserving the soil of their area. Generally the states have given the districts two types of powers. The first is a series of activities necessary for carrying on a voluntary conservation program. The second is the power to prescribe several types of compulsory land-use regulations to prevent and control erosion.

Included in the first series of activities which the districts were to be authorized to undertake, according to the standard act, were: carrying on research in erosion control; conducting demonstrational projects; carrying out prevention and control measures; entering into contracts with farmers and giving them financial and other assistance; acquiring, using, and disposing of property; making loans and gifts of equipment, machinery, seeds, and so on to farmers; taking over and operating state and federal erosion-control projects; constructing and maintaining structures; developing land-use plans, accepting contributions of money, services, materials; and imposing conditions on the extension of benefits.

With the exception of a few states, the functions given the

districts by each state are largely those marked out in the standard act. Although there is considerable variety in district powers granted by the state enabling acts, each state has generally granted to its districts almost all of the authorities specified in the standard act. Fourteen states have authorized their districts to carry on activities virtually identical to those set forth in the standard act. These states are Alabama, Florida, Maryland, Minnesota, Montana, Nebraska, Nevada, New Mexico, North Dakota, South Carolina, Utah, Vermont, Virginia, and Wyoming.

Four states, Arkansas, Louisiana, North Carolina, and South Dakota, confer on their districts all of the powers of the standard act, except those of carrying on research or conducting demonstrations. Ten other states, whose laws include other deviations from the standard act, fail to grant specifically either one or both of these powers. California omits research from its listing of district activities. Kentucky, Massachusetts, New York, and Ohio delete the carrying on of demonstration projects. Illinois, Maine, Missouri, Texas, and Wisconsin fail to specify either power.

The standard act does not empower the district to tax or to incur bonded indebtedness. Only districts in California and Colorado enjoy a general taxing power in their own right. The power of eminent domain, which is not provided in the standard act, is granted to districts only in Arkansas and California.

California and Tennessee do not specifically grant the districts the power to extend financial aid to cooperating farmers. Two other states, New Hampshire and Ohio, do not specifically give the districts the authority to furnish farmers either financial aid or materials and equipment. Again, New Hampshire and Ohio do not give the districts authority to acquire, use and dispose of property. In Massachusetts and New York, the acquisition of property is limited to necessary equipment, materials, machinery and personal property. Ohio and Kansas do not give their districts the authority to construct and maintain structures ". . . necessary or convenient for the performance of any operation authorized in this act." In Mississippi, such structures can be built and maintained only ". . . with the consent of two-thirds of the landowners owning sixty-six and two-thirds per cent of all lands affected." Four states, Arizona, Colorado, New Hampshire and Ohio, do not grant districts authority to impose conditions upon farmers for the extension of benefits to them.

The power which the states most generally failed to confer on their districts is that of adopting and enforcing compulsory land-use regulations. Sixteen states now refuse their districts this authority. These states are: Arizona, California, Connecticut, Delaware, Idaho, Indiana, Iowa, Maine, Massachusetts, Michigan, Missouri, New Hampshire, New York, Ohio, Pennsylvania, and Rhode Island. This was the power which the Service originally felt was most necessary for the districts to possess, if they were to serve effectively in the local carrying out of a nation-wide conservation program.[4]

Perhaps the most significant deviation from the federal standard act in its effect upon district independence of the national agency has been the trend in district laws to give a state body — usually the state soil conservation committee or the land-grant college — some additional authority over district operations.[5] This may ultimately result in the limiting of districts' local independence. But responsibility to a state level is a typical characteristic of local government. Moreover, the placing of a state agency between the federal government and the local districts may eventually serve to lessen federal guidance in local soil conservation administration.

Exercise of District Powers by Local Supervisors

The exercising of the district's powers through officially designated local people is still another characteristic of local government to be found in the soil conservation district. The district board of supervisors — ordinarily composed of three farmers elected in the district and two local farmers appointed by the state committee — serves as the governing body and exercises those powers granted the district by state law. That these powers are sometimes restricted by the requirements of referenda or state committee approval already has been explained. Within the limits of these restrictions, the district board of supervisors is legally empowered to function in much the same manner as the governing body of any other local government.

DISTRICT DEPENDENCE UPON NATIONAL GOVERNMENT

Although the legal, structural independence of the district is the foundation block in the evolving governmental arrangements for achieving soil conservation, the whole purpose and orientation

---

[4] For fuller discussion, see Chapter 6.
[5] For fuller discussion, see Chapter 7.

of the district is radically different from that of the traditional units of local government. The district was not designed to act in isolation. Rather it was to be a governmental apparatus which would bring together into an ordered, common effort the competencies, energies, and resources of public agencies functioning in soil conservation. Fundamental, therefore, in the operation of the districts has been their selective acceptance of the material assistance of a variety of public agencies, private groups, and individuals.

Thus far it has been the extensive assistance given the districts by the Soil Conservation Service, prime mover in the creation of the district mechanism, which has made them effective going concerns. The Soil Conservation Service has in varying degrees provided locally organized farmers with the technical assistance, soil conserving equipment, and planting stock which has made local soil conservation operations possible.[6] This thought was expressed in an exchange between Senator Russell, of Georgia, and E. C. McArthur, late president of the National Association of Soil Conservation Districts, in hearings on the 1948 agricultural appropriation bill:

SENATOR RUSSELL: Therefore, the whole movement, if it did not have the assistance that the Federal Government provides, would have no conservation work. You would still have your districts, but you would not have a conservation work going on within the districts.

MR. McARTHUR: That is exactly right, sir. In other words, I would like to elaborate a little bit. The Soil Conservation Service is the very life blood of the districts. Everything depends upon it.[7]

Technical Competence

The chief contribution which the Soil Conservation Service makes to farmers locally organized for conservation is technical competence for planning and applying conservation practices and measures. H. H. Bennett sees the Service as:

. . . essentially . . . a corps of trained, experienced specialists in land, plants, animals, and land use, organized to work cooperatively with farmers out on their land, chiefly by supplying technical assistance,

---

[6] During the early days of the soil conservation program, when the CCC camps were still in operation, CCC labor was sometimes provided farmers to aid them in applying conservation practices.

[7] U. S. Congress. Senate Committee on Appropriations. *Hearings before the Subcommittee on the Agriculture Department Appropriation Bill for 1948.* 80th Cong., 2nd Sess., p. 1117.

all the way from planning the work to helping with its application and maintenance.[8]

The planning and application of measures and practices for conserving the soil of a farm demands knowledge in agronomy, engineering, biology, forestry, hydrology, and other specialized fields. "Since farming is a full-time business," SCS points out, "few farmers have the time to perfect themselves in each of these important fields. Obviously, the farmer will need technical help in carrying out practices in these various fields. It is hardly practical to expect that it would be possible, by any educational processes known, to give to the farmer in a short time all the information he might need in solving all the problems he would be sure to encounter. That is why the Soil Conservation Service has a staff of technicians with years of training and added years of actual experience in their various fields of work."[9]

The Soil Conservation Service reported that it furnished, during the calendar year of 1951, a total of 7,900 professional-and subprofessional-man years of personnel below the state level. This staff includes district conservationists, work unit leaders, farm planners, soil surveyors, specialists, and aids, whose chief job is aiding farmers in planning, applying, and maintaining conservation practices. [10] On an average, there were 3.3 SCS field technicians in each district in 1951. The national Service also maintains a corps of research men for the continuing study of soil conserving practices and techniques.

In addition to its technical assistance in conservation planning and application, the Service has developed a special experience and knowledge in administrative arrangements and procedures for putting a conservation program into successful operation within an area.

Few conservation districts or local or county governments in

[8] H. H. Bennett, "Planning for Soil Conservation," *Soil Conservation.* Vol. XI, January 1946, p. 154.

[9] *Report of the Chief of the Soil Conservation Service*, 1946, p. 3.

[10] SCS, "Analysis of Soil Conservation Service Work in Conservation Districts, calendar year, 1951." Administratively, the line of authority is from the chief of the Service to the regional director to the state conservationist to the district conservationist (the work group leader) and the work unit conservationist. The work unit is the Service's basic organization unit, and a farm conservation planner, who is designated as a work unit conservationist, serves as its leader. The size of the work unit is variable, depending upon the potential work load, difficulty of the conservation job, and so forth. But some idea of size can be had from the fact that the work unit in Tennessee and Wisconsin conforms with the boundaries of a county. Likewise, the work group is composed of a variable number of work units. Again, for illustration, the work group in Tennessee and Wisconsin is usually composed of four or five counties.

the United States would feel financially capable of hiring a farm planner and any necessary sub-professional assistance to aid them in conserving the soil of their area. Probably only a minority of the states would attempt to finance a program providing such specialized technical assistance to their rural communities. Although many of the state agricultural experiment stations are carrying on productive research into soil conserving practices, the national government has brought into this research activity personnel, material resources, and a broad coverage in varying experience which would not otherwise have been available.

Conservation Equipment and Planting Stock

In addition to furnishing technical knowledge, the Soil Conservation Service, in the earlier years of district development, provided the districts with a major portion of its conservation equipment. J. C. Dykes, the assistant chief of the Service, estimated in 1946 that SCS had in the past provided the districts with a good portion of their equipment.[11] When queried by Congressman Tarver, Dykes indicated, in 1944 that the maximum equipment which SCS would provide a district would not exceed three to five thousand dollars.[12] Besides making available to the districts the equipment used in the Service's program of demonstration projects and the equipment used by the CCC camps, the Conservation Service, through funds appropriated by Congress, purchased equipment for grant and loan to the districts. In 1947, two and a half million dollars were earmarked for the purchase of federal surplus equipment to be loaned to the districts. Since 1947 Congress has made no funds available for the purchase of equipment. The recent trend has been for SCS to: ". . . get out of the equipment field."[13]

A third type of material assistance which the Soil Conservation Service gives the district is a limited amount of planting stock, such as trees, shrubs, and grass and legume seeds. The Service furnishes planting materials: ". . . only if they are either (i) improved or uncommon, or (ii) not generally within the economic reach of owners and operators of land within the district, or (iii)

---

[11] U. S. Congress. House Committee on Appropriations. *Hearings before the Subcommittee on the Agriculture Department Appropriation Bill for 1947.* 79th Cong., 2nd Sess., p. 1052.

[12] U. S. Congress. House Committee on Appropriations. *Hearings before the Subcommittee on the Agriculture Department Appropriation Bill for 1945.* 78th Cong., 2nd Sess., p. 1080.

[13] For fuller discussion, see Chapter 4.

Fig. 1 — A dramatic manifestation of erosion is seen in these gullies found in Georgia. The gullies affect an area of more than 100,000 acres, and range in depth from 50 to 200 feet.

Fig. 2 — Very active gullies in Mississippi. A 13-year study showed that gullies similar to these yielded 300 tons of silt and sand per acre per year.

materials particularly necessary to prove or demonstrate measures
or practices appropriate for erosion control and soil conservation
work." [14]

In accordance with the SCS policy of reducing to a minimum
the material assistance given soil conservation districts, the practice
of furnishing cooperating farmers with nursery planting stock in
quantity is being gradually discontinued. Whereas in 1940 a total
of 143,000,000 trees were produced in SCS nurseries, in 1945 only
57,000,000 were produced. This number was further reduced to
about 18,500,000 in 1950.[15] Because of the serious national short-
age of grass and legume seeds, SCS nurseries have been cooperating
with the Bureau of Plant Industry, Soils and Agricultural Engineering, and the state agricultural experiment stations in pro-
ducing and distributing seeds of improved soil conserving forage
crops. During the fiscal year 1946, approximately 500,000 pounds
of high quality seed were produced in SCS nurseries.[16] In 1950,
SCS seed output had increased to 2,400,000 pounds.[17]

As measured by financial outlays, the national government's
contribution to the operation of each soil conservation district
through the Soil Conservation Service averaged $23,000 in 1951.
The cost per district has run as high as $32,862 in 1940, and as
low as $20,494 in 1944. The Service estimates that the federal
government spends about $500 to aid a farmer plan and apply a
conservation program to his land. The Service reported that in
1951 its cost per acre for conservation planning and application
was $1.69.[18]

Agricultural Conservation Payments

Although the federal government has channeled its direct
assistance to the districts through the Soil Conservation Service,
its second major conservation program, the Agricultural Conservation Program of the Production and Marketing Administration, has indirectly given a financial subsidy to the work of
the districts.

The conservation program of the PMA has been the result of
two historical accidents — a Supreme Court decision and a world

[14] "Principles and Procedures," *Soil Conservation Service Manual,* No. 49212.2,
February 2, 1942, p. cont'd. 2.
[15] Letter from C. L. Orrben, Acting Chief, Project Plans Division, SCS, to author,
September 12, 1950.
[16] *Report of the Chief of the Soil Conservation Service,* 1946, pp. 32, 33.
[17] Letter from C. L. Orrben, cited.
[18] Administrative records, SCS files. This figure includes all overhead cost.

war — rather than the product of careful administrative planning. When the U. S. Supreme Court invalidated the first AAA program on the grounds that the federal government did not have the constitutional authority to control agricultural production,[19] the federal government, in 1936, improvised the Soil Conservation and Domestic Allotment Act. The new law made production control incidental to soil conservation. Acreage control was to be achieved indirectly through soil conservation. Instead of direct bounties for cutting production, benefit payments were made to farmers who cooperated in a soil conservation program, which shifted land from soil-depleting crops to a variety of cover crops. Payment to a farmer was made upon the basis of the amount of cultivated acreage he shifted over to legumes or pasturage.

Although direct production controls through a marketing quota system were reinstated in the 1938 agricultural production act, soil conservation benefit payments were continued as a secondary means of adjusting the production of soil depleting crops. National acreage allotments were determined individually for the soil-depleting crops — cotton, corn, wheat, rice, tobacco, peanuts, and potatoes — and as a group for others. The national allotments were then apportioned among the individual farms. Compliance with his allotment by the individual farmer was purely voluntary. But, if he complied, the farmer became a cooperator entitled to adjustment payments.

With World War II the national need became that of increasing production. However, so firmly entrenched was the soil conservation adjustment payment as a farmer income supplement that politically it could not be abandoned. Therefore, since 1943 production control has not been tied to the funds Congress has appropriated each year for payments to farmers for carrying out soil building and soil and water conserving practices.

The extent to which the agriculture conservation payment has made it financially possible for farmers to cooperate in the district program cannot be accurately estimated. The new chief of the Soil Conservation Service, Robert Salter, recently stressed the need for giving farmers financial assistance in making adjustments to conservation farming:

A well-planned program for conservation farming on most farms comprises practices the application of which requires considerable capital investment. Moreover, shifts to conservation farming often

---

[19] United States v. Butler, 279 U. S. 1 (1936) .

require temporary economic sacrifices since some time may be needed for returns from the new system to equal and exceed the old system. For example, on many farms in the Southeast, shifting from single-crop farming to conservation farming including livestock requires fencing, livestock, buildings, and equipment. Many farmers require financial assistance in order to put conservation farming into practice.

The development of forms of public and private credit better geared to the repayment potentials of conservation farming would aid materially on many farms. On the other hand, on some farms in most areas, and on most farms in some areas, the financial requirements exceed available resources. It may require many years for these farmers to pull themselves up by their own bootstraps. I doubt if the Nation can afford to wait that long and permit our soil resources to further deteriorate in the process. I am convinced that the urgency of the national interest justifies the Government sharing the costs of conservation as provided under the agricultural conservation program.[20]

Approximately $285,000,000 was paid farmers in conservation payments during the fiscal year 1952.[21] How much of these payments went to farmers who were carrying out a farm conservation plan under the district program is not known. Officials of both the Soil Conservation Service and the Production and Marketing Adminstration have agreed, under Congressional questioning, that the ACP payments have financially supplemented the work of the districts "significantly." A deputy director of PMA explains:

We do not have statistical information on the extent to which conservation payments under the Agricultural Conservation program have been made on all practices called for under Soil Conservation District farm plans. The Agricultural Conservation Program for a county does not offer program payments on all the needed conservation measures which farmers carry out. . . . We believe that county agricultural programs include the conservation measures most commonly called for in the farm plans. . . . Farmers who are carrying out conservation plans developed for their farms by the Soil Conservation District naturally tend to use the assistance available to their farms under the ACP for the accomplishment of those plans.[22]

The considerable extent to which ACP payments have been going to district cooperators in the past has recently been indicated by the fact that 100,000 of the 240,000 ACP farmers who

---

[20] U. S. Congress. House Committee on Appropriations. *Hearings before the Subcommittee on the Agriculture Department Appropriation Bill for 1953.* 82nd Cong., 2nd Sess., p. 508.

[21] *Ibid.,* p. 1259.

[22] Letter from Thomas B. Joyce, Deputy Director, Production and Marketing Administration, to author, March 27, 1951.

were referred by PMA committees to SCS for technical assistance, in accordance with the 1951 departmental reorganization order, were already district cooperators.[23] Under the departmental reorganization called for by Secretary Brannan on February 15, 1951, there is a much closer integration of the conservation payment program and the district's program for extending technical conservation assistance and the use of equipment to farmers.[24] According to Undersecretary McCormick:

> The spirit and intent of the Secretary's Memorandum Number 1278 is the coordination of agricultural resources, conservation policies and programs of Department agencies into a single agricultural resources conservation program. . . . Joint formulation and determination of policies and programs at all levels will result in a single over-all program toward which all agencies would direct their efforts.[25]

The basic objective toward which all of the soil conservation activities of the federal department are to work is: ". . . the use of each acre of agricultural land within its capabilities and the treatment of each acre of agricultural land in accordance with its needs for protection and improvement." To achieve this goal, the agricultural resources conservation agencies, although not consolidated into a single agency, have been put under the supervision and direction of an assistant secretary.[26] The Secretary's memorandum specifies that:

> . . . under the direction of the Assistant Secretary, the Soil Conservation Service, the Forest Service, and the Production and Marketing Administration will jointly determine the soil conservation practices to be included in the Agricultural Conservation Program, and rates of payments for soil conservation practices, by meetings and consultations at the national, State, and county levels. All agencies shall be guided by the Department's basic soil conservation objective.[27]

The federal soil conservation program for each state is to be jointly developed by the state representatives of PMA, SCS, and the Forest Service. The Land-Grant College and the Farmers Home Administration also are invited to serve with this committee. The county program committees are to be similarly

---

[23] House Appropriation *Hearings,* 1953, *op. cit.,* p. 511.
[24] Memorandum Number 1278 of Secretary of Agriculture, Charles F. Brannan, "Coordination of the Department's Agricultural Resources Conservation Services," February 15, 1951.
[25] Memorandum of C. J. McCormick, "Development of State and County Agricultural Conservation Program," March 22, 1951.
[26] Secretary of Agriculture, Memorandum 1278, *op. cit.*
[27] *Ibid.*

constituted of county representatives of the various agencies, plus the governing body of the soil conservation district.

Each agency is to be responsible for the administration of its own program, as it has been worked out in joint consultation with the other agencies. However, the Soil Conservation Service also is made responsible for all technical phases of the permanent type of soil conservation work.[28] Included in the permanent type of conservation work are such practices as terraces, permanent sod waterways, constructing permanent riprap, establishing strip cropping, constructing dams, ponds, land leveling, and installing or improving drainage systems.

Acting upon the basis of the Secretary's order, the chiefs of SCS and PMA have jointly determined that the Service's responsibility for the technical phases of conservation includes:

(1) a finding by SCS that the permanent type soil conservation work contemplated is needed and practical on the farm, (2) necessary site selection, other preliminary work, and layout work of the practices, (3) the necessary supervision of the installation, and (4) certification of performance (or application of the practice on the land).[29]

To meet its new technical responsibilities, the Service has designated one of its farm planners in each county as the SCS employee primarily responsible for working in the consolidated county program.

Because of the new role of SCS employees and the district supervisors in helping to formulate the over-all county conservation program, the practices carried on by the districts and the PMA county committees should more closely coincide. Moreover, SCS technicians in rendering assistance to ACP farmers are to encourage these farmers to become participants in the district program. Thus, the assistance the ACP indirectly gives the districts will likely be larger in the future.

Although farmers cooperating in the district program may receive substantial financial assistance in their conservation work through the ACP payments, the Agricultural Conservation Program of PMA has no direct financial relationships with the district as such. Therefore, district independence has in no way been circumscribed by any financial assistance PMA may have indirectly

---

[28] Joint Memorandum from G. F. Geissler, Administrator, PMA and H. H. Bennett, Chief, SCS, to Chairman, State PMA Committees and Regional Directors and State Conservationists, SCS, "Responsibilities in Connection with 1951 Agricultural Conservation Program under Secretary's Memorandum 1278," April 3, 1951.

[29] *Ibid.*

been lending the district program. The Soil Conservation Service, however, makes its grants of technical assistance, conservation equipment, and planting stock directly to the districts. It depends upon the districts to use these resources effectively. Therefore, district dependence upon the Soil Conservation Service for its material assistance has necessarily meant some limitation upon district independence as a local government.

The Soil Conservation Service feels it must require minimum levels of adequacy of local performance. The need is not so much to prevent the dishonest or illegal local use of federal resources. Rather the problem is to obtain the effective local carrying out of a nation-wide conservation program in return for federal assistance in achieving the local program. The critical quizzing of SCS officials by the House Agricultural Appropriations Sub-committee in 1949, 1950, and again in 1951, illustrates how completely Congress fixes responsibility for conservation upon the federal agency. The Soil Conservation Service, rather than the local districts, was challenged by the committee on the rate of conservation accomplishment.

CHAPTER 3

Gearing Local Districts Into National Conservation Program

Basic in any effort to organize for national action is the problem of how the field activities can be effectively directed and co-ordinated. The task of the Soil Conservation Service in organizing for operation in the localities has been more difficult than that of a national agency relying entirely upon its own bureaucracy to carry out its program. Although the local district does not fit the pattern of a traditional unit of local government, local determination is still the basic foundation block in the nation-wide district program. The problem in developing a nation-wide conservation effort has been that of organizing and operating an effective national program without sacrificing the local districts' control over their programs.

How were Service-district relationships to be so organized that the millions of farmers in the United States, working in hundreds of conservation districts, would eventually apply adequate conservation treatments to each acre of rural land? Through what procedures could the Service: (1) obtain in the districts an administrative organization and working process which was adequate for managing local soil conserving activities; and (2) give the districts that minimum of operational guidance which was seen by the Service as necessary for obtaining effective nation-wide conservation? How could district conservation activities be fitted into a national administration without losing the advantages of adjustment to local circumstances and local determination and management of conservation activities? How were the districts to be persuaded to accept and abide by nationally established obligations of specific performance?

FEDERAL INFLUENCE ON STATE ENABLING LAWS

As creatures of the state, the districts' organization and functions are prescribed by their respective state enabling acts. Thus the first necessity, as seen by the Service, in bringing the districts into a national conservation program was the enactment of suitable state conservation laws. That is, the need was for laws which permitted the districts to operate in such a way that they could effectively carry their local responsibilities in soil conservation.

So that the districts might conform to a relatively uniform national pattern in their administrations, the Department of Agriculture suggested to the states a standard state act for authorizing the organization and operation of districts. With so many legislative bodies having the authority to determine the framework within which local conservation activity was to be undertaken, it was to be expected that, despite the model act, no national pattern in local conservation administration could be approximated without some national coercion.

Under the authority of the federal soil conservation act of 1935, the Department, early in 1937, began making determinations as to: "... whether each [state] law was such as to merit cooperation by the Department agencies with the districts organized thereunder, and, if so, the types of assistance that were warranted,"[1] In December 1938, this procedure was formalized in a memorandum approved by the Secretary into a system of categories of assistance. The amount of assistance to be furnished by the Service to the districts within a state was to depend upon the adequacy of the state soil conservation district law: "... to authorize activities to carry out a well-rounded soil conservation and erosion control program." [2] The states were grouped into three categories for assistance for the purpose of determining the amount of aid to be furnished the district.

The states falling within the first group were those whose laws: "... embody the basic principles of the Department's recommended Standard State Soil Conservation Districts Law." In the second group were those states whose laws: "... embody substantially the basic principles of the Standard State Soil Con-

---

[1] Memorandum from H. H. Bennett to the Secretary of Agriculture, "Broadening, for the Duration, Types of Assistance SCS May Make Available to Soil Conservation Districts in Certain States," June 24, 1942, p. 1.
[2] "Principles and Procedures," *Soil Conservation Service Manual,* No. 49210, September 21, 1940, p. 1.

servation Districts Law, but which contain provisions which raise administrative or legal problems." Finally, there were those states whose laws: ". . . deviate in certain major respects from the Standard State Soil Conservation Districts Law." [3]

A district within the first group of states was to receive all the needed types of Service assistance that available resources permitted, as soon as the district had met the administrative requirements laid down by the Service. The second group was also to receive full assistance. The Service explained its reason for extending this group full assistance, thus:

It is expected that experience with districts organized under the soil conservation districts laws of the States included in Group II will reveal a need for amendments to those laws, but at the present time the Soil Conservation Service is not prepared to conclude that a well-rounded erosion control program cannot be effectively carried out under them. It is therefore recommended that, until such time as experience shows that a complete coordinated erosion control program cannot be carried out by districts organized in the States included in this group, the same types of assistance be extended to such districts as to districts organized under the laws of the States included in Group I.[4]

The Service did not believe, however, that the districts organized under laws in the third group would:

. . . have sufficient authority to carry out a complete erosion control program. In addition to other defects, those laws contain one common defect, i.e., lack of authority in the districts to conduct a program providing adequately for enforcement of land-use regulations. . . . In view of the inadequacy of these laws, it is recommended that . . . the furnishing of Departmental equipment and planting materials be specifically withheld from districts . . . until such time as the statutes can be appropriately amended.[5]

The Service, in 1942, in reviewing its use of its categories of assistance was convinced that the differentials in assistance had served as a leverage in persuading the states to adopt suitable enabling legislation. It cited the laws of Montana, North Dakota, Vermont, and Indiana as cases in point. Nevertheless, at the time when the categories were discontinued for the war period, eight states were still in group three. These states were

---

[3] Memorandum from H. H. Bennett to the Secretary of Agriculture, "Recommendations as to Departmental Cooperation with Soil Conservation Districts Organized under Existing State Soil Conservation Districts Laws," December 1, 1938, p. 2.

[4] *Ibid.*, p. 3.

[5] *Ibid.*, pp. 3, 4.

Arizona, Idaho, Iowa, Maine, Minnesota, Nebraska, New York, and Ohio. Moreover, the states recently passing enabling acts and several states amending their laws have departed even more radically from the standard acts.[6]

In the need for maximum production of food and fiber for the war effort, the Service temporarily abandoned its policy of distributing aid according to adequacy of state laws. Since the categories of assistance have not been reestablished, the Service now considers all states eligible for full assistance. Apparently the Service has discovered that it is able to obtain the development of a district organization and working process adequate for carrying on soil conserving activity without the state laws following the model pattern.

DISTRICT ACCEPTANCE OF MINIMUM NATIONAL STANDARDS

In organizing its work with the districts, the Service sought to develop a procedure for so guiding the organization and operations of the districts that the individual farmers working within a district could be led to establish conservation practices of a uniformly high level of technical adequacy without sacrificing an optimum of local district determination. The procedure SCS developed was first to lay down a national floor of minimum essentials which it believed were so necessary for effective conservation that they must always be present before national assistance could be extended or continued. These essentials divide roughly into two groups: (1) those calculated to make each farmer receiving public conservation assistance an effective and responsible agent in soil conservation; and (2) those designed to provide the district with an administration effective enough to bring all the rural acres within the district eventually under adequate conservation treatment.

The second part of the Service procedure was to give its regional offices the authority to establish measurements for determining whether each district was adequately meeting the minimum national requirements. The regional office could insist that a district agree to additional performance obligations, before it would certify that the district had met the national requirements sufficiently for the Service to commit itself to definite assistance. Thus, through this authority of the regional office to interpret and adjust minimum national essentials to each individual district, each district can be committed to high standards of performance adjusted to the peculiar needs and circumstances of its area.

---

[6] *See* Chapter 6.

The means by which the Service attempts to develop and maintain these standards of performance are threefold. The first is the use of a series of formal documents and agreements, which progressively and more specifically commit a district to a framework of positive obligations. Simultaneously these argreements progressively commit the Department and the Service to rendering definite assistance. Secondly, the Service suggests to the districts a variety of prefabricated working forms and procedures to use in carrying on their activities. It also cooperates in providing — usually through the agency of the state committees — operational guides and handbooks which advise on the best district working methods. In the third place, Service personnel working with the districts may in propriety suggest lines of action to district governing bodies. All three of these means are, of course, combined in the Service's effort to give the districts that minimum of national guidance which it considers necessary if every district is adequately to carry out its local share in the national task.

Use of Working Documents and Agreements

The first step in establishing the respective responsibilities and obligations of the Department and a district is their entering into a formal memorandum of understanding. As H. H. Bennett has said, such a memorandum does little more than reduce to writing the intention of the parties to cooperate in a soil conservation program. Although the memorandum does not commit the Department or any of its agencies to furnishing assistance to a district, the Department calls for its first minimum requirement of the district as a prerequisite to its signing of a memorandum.

DISTRICT PROGRAM

Before a memorandum can be entered into, the district must have developed a district program. That is, it must have established its goals and objectives in conservation. The Department itself takes: ". . . no responsibility for the completeness or soundness of the [district] program and will neither approve nor disapprove it." [7] However, the Department does not enter into such a memorandum of understanding with a district until at least one agency within the Department has determined, on the basis of the district program, that it can render the district assistance. "Each agency will be free," explained the Secretary, "upon

---

[7] "A Statement by the Secretary of Agriculture Concerning Departmental Cooperation with Soil Conservation Districts," *op. cit.,* p. cont'd. 4.

examining the program to determine the degree to which it will assist the district toward carrying out that program. . . . It is possible that a particular program . . . may be inadequate to enable a particular Departmental agency to cooperate with the district. In such cases, any agency may consult with the district concerning appropriate modifications in the program." [8] Thus, the Soil Conservation Service, always the first departmental agency to cooperate with districts, can make a determination concerning the adequacy of a district's goals and objectives.

The national office of the Service sets up no minimum standards or essentials for the contents of a district program. Although a district's program flows up through the state and regional offices to Washington, where it is given a review in three offices — the solicitor's office, project plans division of SCS, and the Secretary's office — the review is cursory. In recent years the Service, as one SCS official puts it, has only required that there be some sort of a conservation program.

That there are no national minimum requirements for a district's program is evidenced by the wide variations in the content, length and terminology of the more than 2,400 accepted district programs. Recently the Service has accepted programs from several districts in North Dakota which were merely preliminary two- or three-page reports, which pointed out in large terms the conservation problems of the district with the understanding that a more comprehensive program was later to be developed.

Despite the Service's no longer requiring the inclusion of certain items in a district's program, it still largely influences the content of the programs. Although SCS has discontinued the circulation of a long, detailed outline to be used as a basis for program preparation, both the Washington and regional offices offer guiding suggestions for preparing a district's program. The Washington office has an official guide which leadingly discusses the district program's purpose and use, the procedures for developing the program, and the desirable contents of the program.[9] The SCS regional offices have usually supplemented the Washington statement with more detailed suggestions.[10]

---

[8] *Ibid.*, p. cont'd. 4.

[9] "District Program and Work Plan," *Soil Conservation Service Manual*, No. 49130, pp. 1—cont'd. 4.

[10] The numerical designation, title, and state composition of the seven SCS regions are as follows: Region I—Northeastern; includes Connecticut, Delaware, Maine, Maryland, Massachusetts, New Hampshire, New Jersey, New York, Pennsylvania, Rhode Island, Vermont, and West Virginia. Region II—Southeastern;

These guides and suggestions are not distributed to district governing bodies, but to SCS personnel working in the districts. Indeed, the most effective way in which the national agency secures the adoption of adequate district goals and objectives is through the personal influence of its field men, who can be given uniform central instructions. Service personnel are usually assigned to a district as soon as the governing body of the district is organized, that is, before either the program or work plan has been developed. The Service, through written guides and the guiding assistance of the field staff, can still largely influence the form and content of a district's program. But SCS relaxation in program specifications probably reflects the Service's growing thought that a suitable district working process is more important than admirable goals in achieving adequate conservation operations within a district.

MEMORANDUM OF UNDERSTANDING

The first essential in district conservation activity laid down by the federal Department — that of establishing suitable objectives — is, then, a prerequisite to the Department's entering into its first memorandum with the district. In the memorandum itself, the district is committed to further positive actions. First it agrees to develop a definite and systematic working process for achieving erosion control and soil conservation. That is, it agrees to formulate a district work plan. Secondly, the district commits itself to a policy of defining in writing the obligations of farmers receiving federal assistance in conservation and of holding farmers accountable for carrying out their agreed-upon obligations. The Service has believed that this pinning down of farmer responsibility is of critical importance in getting sound conservation practices established by the farmers of the nation. The form of agreement which a district develops for binding the farmer to specific obligations must be acceptable to the cooperating federal agency. In other words, constitutional permission is given the Service to impose more specific additional obligations upon the district and indirectly upon the farmers.

Alabama, Florida, Georgia, Kentucky, Mississippi, North Carolina, South Carolina, Tennessee, and Virginia. Region III—Upper Mississippi; Illinois, Indiana, Iowa, Michigan, Minnesota, Missouri, Ohio, and Wisconsin. Region IV—Western Gulf; Arkansas, Louisiana, Oklahoma, and Texas. Region V—Northern Great Plains; Kansas, Montana, Nebraska, North Dakota, South Dakota, and Wyoming. Region VI—Southwestern; Arizona, Colorado, New Mexico, and Utah. Region VII—Pacific; California, Idaho, Nevada, Oregon, and Washington. Hereafter, SCS regions and regional offices will usually be referred to only by their numerical designations, e.g., "Region I," and so forth.

Finally, the district promises to give the Department information on how it is carrying out its agreed-upon program and working process. Not only does a district agree to report annually upon its activities and accomplishments, but it is to keep its records in such a way that the agencies of the Department cooperating with the district may obtain adequate information as to the district activities more frequently than once a year by examining these records. The district also is to inform cooperating agencies of any substantial changes in its program or work plan.[11]

DISTRICT WORK PLAN

Just as the prerequisite for entering into the first basic agreement was an acceptable district program, so the development of a district work plan is the prerequisite to the Service's committing itself, in a supplemental memorandum of understanding, to making its assistance available to a district. The work plan — or working process — is to be:

> . . . a presentation, at any one time, of the proposed conservation practices and methods for effectuating their application upon lands within the district, the current plan of district activities and procedures for carrying on such activities, and who, if any individual or agency, will assist the district in such activities — all in the interest of carrying out the objectives of the program.[12]

The Washington office believes that a work plan: ". . . should provide a general answer, at any one time, regardng district activities, as to what is to be done, and where, when, how, and by whom."[13] As a guide to its field personnel the Washington staff outlines in general terms a district work plan which includes: ". . . not only a presentation of practices to be put into operation but . . . also . . . plans for and priorities of work by areas, plans for educational activities, responsibilities of supervisors, agencies, and farmers in carrying out plans of work and provision for revision of the work plan." [14]

In their procedural guides to state and district personnel, the regional offices have laid down more specific suggestions in developing a plan of work. Accordingly, SCS field men aiding the

---

[11] "Memorandum of Understanding between the ——— Soil Conservation District, State of ——— and the United States Department of Agriculture," *Soil Conservation Service Manual*, No. 49120, p. cont'd.

[12] "District Program and Work Plan," *Soil Conservation Service Manual, op. cit.,* p. cont'd. 4.

[13] *Ibid.,* p. cont'd. 5.

[14] *Ibid.,* p. cont'd. 6.

governing bodies in developing their work plans usually suggest the inclusion of minimum practices adequate to meet the conservation needs of the various types of land classes, the most effective methods for planning and applying conservation measures, the establishment of minimum responsibilities for cooperating farmers, minimums in conservation plans, and so on.

A district's governing body is free to accept or reject any Service suggestions. As Mr. Dykes, the assistant chief of SCS, explained to Senator Russell: "It is the district's plan, and it is not a Federal agency plan or State agency plan. We don't have the privilege, and we don't want the privilege of saying that you have got to put this and that in your district program and plan." But, as Mr. Dykes had already pointed out: "Now, if any of the Federal agencies, or the State agencies, don't like it, they don't have to cooperate with the districts." [15] If a district's plan of work, in the regional director's judgment, does not provide in general a satisfactory basis for making assistance available, the Service will not enter into a supplemental memorandum of understanding.[16]

Here again, the only national essential laid down is that there be a district work plan. However, by giving the regional director the authority to evaluate the adequacy of the work plan, the Service may establish, on the regional level, certain essentials which must be present in a district's working process. The extent to which the regional office spells out items to be included in district work plans varies from region to region. Districts in Region II, for example, have always had wide discretion in determining the contents of their work plans. In contrast, Region IV has given the districts comparatively little latitude. In that region, a seventy-five-page outline has specified just what was to be included in a district's plan. That the regional offices, in the past, have generally insisted upon certain essentials being incorporated in a district's work plan is evidenced by the fact that there have been definite regional differences in the techniques and methods set up in district work plans.

The recent policy in most regions, however, has been to encourage the districts to use more discretion in preparing their documents. Because the regional offices found that they were

---

[15] U. S. Congress. Senate Committee on Appropriations. *Hearings before the Subcommittee on the Agriculture Department Appropriation Bill for 1945.* 78th Cong., 2nd Sess., p. 410.

[16] "Principles and Procedures," *Soil Conservation Service Manual,* No. 49212.1, p. cont'd.

merely getting back their own outline of suggestions for a district work plan, several regions have either abbreviated their work plan suggestions or have discontinued their circulation. Moreover, the regions are increasingly accepting, as the basis for cooperation, brief plans in which the districts speak of their intentions only in general terms, which commit the districts to no definite policies. Region VI accepted the work plan of the Alpine District, Utah, which specifically declared that it was not committing itself to any permanent policies until it had gained further experience:

> Due to lack of experience, the policy of this district is not as yet stable. We do not know exactly the plan we should carry out. However, we have decided on some temporary policies which are to govern our activities for the present.

The new trend toward combining relatively short programs and work plans and then supplementing them with annual work plans is a further indication of regional relaxation of specifications for work plans.

SUPPLEMENTAL MEMORANDUM OF UNDERSTANDING

In the supplemental memorandum, the district reaffirms and makes more specific the obligations it accepts in the basic memorandum. The district specifically promises that it:

> ... will utilize assistance made available by the Service only (a) on land under cooperative or working agreements with the District, or (b) on land owned or leased by the District for which a plan of conservation operations has been adopted by the District.[17]

In addition to reporting generally on its conservation activities, the district here pledges itself to keeping current records on the kinds and amount of SCS materials used on lands covered by each cooperative agreement. Besides preparing an annual report on the distribution of materials, district records are to be available for inspection by SCS personnel at any time. Finally, the district accepts the Service's authority to impose further obligations upon the district whenever field equipment is made available to it.

The Service, in its turn, pledges itself to make available to the district the technical assistance of at least one staff member. SCS is also to aid the district by providing it with field equipment and

---

[17] "Supplemental Memorandum of Understanding between the ———— Soil Conservation District, State of ———— and the Soil Conservation Service, United States Department of Agriculture." *Soil Conservation Service Manual*, No. 49212.3, February 2, 1942, p. cont'd. 3.

Fig. 3 — Part of a large sand dune area covering approximately 175,000 acres of range land in Texas.

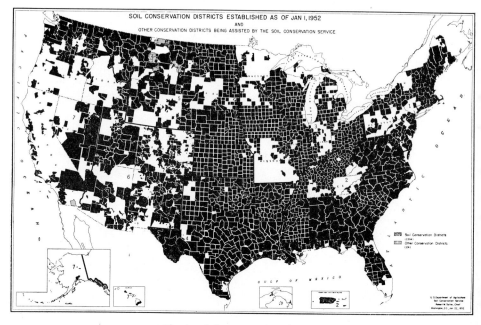

Fig. 4 — Soil conservation districts.

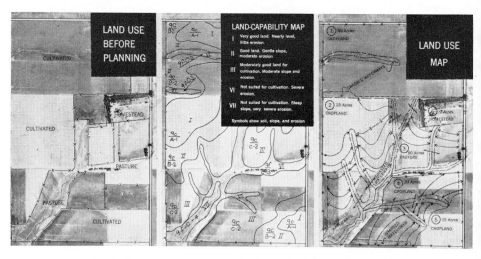

Fig. 5 — Land-use mapping is an aid in developing farm conservation plans.

planting stock whenever it is available in accordance with schedules of assistance, which are later to be prepared.

The two basic memoranda of understanding, then, are in the nature of constitutional authorizing documents. Together with the district program and work plan, they combine into a constitutional framework which permits the Service to require of a district, in constitutional propriety, a series of specific and positive acts in return for the actual extension of Service assistance. Thus, the Service can commit each district to high conservation standards without imposing a national strait-jacket of uniform requirements.

The use of these two memoranda of understanding is not confined to SCS. After the basic memorandum is signed by the Department, any or all of its agencies may sign supplemental memoranda with the districts. Under the Secretary's 1951 arrangement for coordinating the Department's conservation work, other agencies besides SCS may find it increasingly useful to enter into agreements with many of the soil conservation districts.

FARMER-DISTRICT AGREEMENT

Before any assistance is actually made available to a district, the Service requires that district commitments to define and establish adequate responsibilities of a farmer cooperator be satisfactorily carried out. That is, a farmer-district cooperative agreement form, which fixes certain minimum farmer obligations and responsibilities, must be developed.

The 1951 reorganization order of Secretary Brannan, making SCS responsible for the technical phases of the permanent type of soil conservation work carried on by the Department, prompted the Service to relax its minimum requirements for a farmer-district agreement. SCS has suggested to the districts that they so adjust their agreement forms that the ACP farmers whom SCS technicians are assisting can be easily brought into the district program.

In both the old and the new agreement forms, the parties to an agreement are to be identified so that it is clear who assumes the fixed responsibilities. Also, the land on which the conservation plan is to be applied and maintained must be identified. Under the old type agreement, the farmer agreed to be responsible for establishing and continuing the farm's conservation program as planned. The farm plan, which was developed as a prerequisite to the district's entering into the cooperative agreement, marked out what these practices were to be. Finally, the plan agreed upon by the farmer was to be applied within a definite period.[18]

In addition, the Washington office suggested that the districts establish in their agreement forms the responsibility of the farmer to use the assistance made available by the district to accomplish the purposes for which it was furnished. The new agreement forms also are to include this provision. However, they do not specify, as the old ones frequently did, that in the event a farmer:

. . . intentionally fails to fulfill his commitments, the district may at its option terminate the agreement and be reimbursed by the farmer for the value of the labor and materials and the rental value of the equipment made available to him.

Also, to make the responsibilities of the farmer entirely apparent, it was suggested that the form of agreement provide that in the event such assistance is made available, it is to be disposed of and used only as provided in the plan. The new agreement forms also generally carry this provision. The Washington staff further pointed out that it was a:

. . . desirable procedure . . . to establish a schedule (or calendar of operations for the farmer) in relation to the time at which or within which the anticipated assistance will be made available and used. This can be provided for by stating in the agreement that the various operations set forth in the plan are to be completed within the time limits and in the sequence specified in the plan.

Here again in the farmer-district agreement form the national office establishes certain minimum responsibilities which are to be fixed in all cases, and suggests to SCS field personnel other desirable provisions for such agreements. Service field personnel are specifically directed to guide the governing bodies toward fixing an adequate minimum of farmer responsibilities.

Since Service personnel are familiar with various forms of agreements, it is their duty to lead the district governing bodies to realize their responsibilites and help them to determine the essential or desirable conditions of a suitable instrument.[19]

The governing body of the district is free to develop any sort of agreement form it chooses. But until a district has an agreement form which in the SCS regional director's judgement adequately fixes farmer obligations, no Service assistance can be

---

[18] "Farmer-District Cooperative Agreement," *Soil Conservation Service Manual,* No. 49240, pp. 1—cont'd. 9.
[19] *Ibid.,* p. cont'd.

given a farmer in applying practices under the district program. For, as agreed in the two memoranda of understanding, the district is only to utilize Service assistance on land under district-farmer cooperative agreements which are acceptable to SCS. The Upper Mississippi regional office specifically declares that:

. . . under no condition should an SCS technician recommend any developed farm conservation plan to the governing body for approval until the Farmer-District Cooperative Agreement form has been adopted by the district after the other above steps [i.e., submission to, and approval by, the regional office] have been taken.[20]

Since the farmer-district agreements are everywhere regarded as no more than "gentlemen's agreements," the regions have generally not insisted that the provisions recommended by the national office be included. The model agreement suggested by Region VI included only the minimum essential provisions.[21] In California there has been a tendency to omit the time limitation feature. As illustrations, the farmer-district agreement forms of the Big Valley, Romona, San Gorgonio, and Tehachapi Districts were accepted by Region VII despite the fact that they hardly resembled the Service model and set no time limit for the completion of the agreement, which was one of the essentials laid down by the national office.

FARM CONSERVATION PLAN

Within the district the farm plan up until April, 1951, had the same relationship to the farmer-district agreement as, in the area of Service-district relations, the work plan bears to the supplemental memorandum. In any farmer-district agreement form accepted as adequate by the Service, the development of a farm plan was a prerequisite to entering into an agreement. Thus the farmer, to receive Service assistance made available through the district, was required to have his objectives and working procedure specifically outlined and agreed upon in writing.

The Secretary's 1951 reorganization order, as already indicated, has made it expedient for the Service to reappraise its position on the necessity of a farmer's having in his possession a farm plan before he can sign an agreement with the district. In its desire to continue to channel its technical assistance to farmers through the soil conservation district, SCS has found it neces-

---

[20] "Procedure for Guidance in Cooperating with Soil Conservation Districts," SCS Region III, Memorandum No. 11, September 20, 1946, pp. 34, 35.

[21] "Handbook for Farm and Ranch Conservation Planners," SCS Region VI, April, 1946, Sample No. 3849.

sary to modify this requirement. With its limited number of technically trained personnel, it will not be possible for SCS immediately to provide farm plans for all the farmers it is obligated to assist. Therefore, the Service urges:

> That the district governing body adopt as district policy the recognition, as district cooperators, of all those farmers and ranchers who agree:
> 1. To use their land within its capabilities and to treat it in accordance with its needs.
> 2. To develop and carry out a basic conservation plan for their land.[22]

The farmer-district agreement form which has been suggested to Iowa districts by the state soil conservation committee illustrates how this new policy is to be implemented. It runs as follows:

> I am interested in conserving the soil and water on my farm. Therefore, to the best of my ability, I desire to begin using my land within its capability and according to its needs for protection and improvement. I am asking for assistance from the district in working out, putting into effect, and maintaining the conservation practices my land needs that are practical for me to install.
> I will cooperate with the soil conservation district commissioners in working toward the development of a basic farm conservation plan for my entire farm. I will use any materials or equipment made available by the district in the way and for the purpose for which they are furnished.

Under the new procedure which has been suggested by SCS, and by 1952, had been adopted by almost all districts, the farmer and take district will take three distinct, but progressive, steps which will culminate in what has always been known as "the farm plan." In the order of progression, they are called the "initial conservation stage," the "advanced conservation stage," and finally, the "basic conservation plan." In his April 9, 1951, memorandum explaining the new procedure, the chief of SCS outlines what each of the three phases requires of the district and the farmer.[23]

On signing the district agreement a farmer is automatically in the initial stage of planning, and the Service helps him immediately with simple practices which he is ready and able to carry out. For example, if he only wants tile drainage, the tech-

---

[22] Memorandum from H. H. Bennett to Regional Directors, State Conservationists, and District Conservationists, "Procedures for Carrying Out SCS Responsibilities under Secretary's Memorandum No. 1278," April 9, 1951.

[23] *Ibid.*

nician will assist, if he thinks the work is practicable. This type of agreement carries with it only a job sheet and the signed agreement between the district and the cooperator.

In the advanced stage of planning the farmer is in process of developing a basic plan. He moves from the initial stage to the advanced stage on receipt of a land capability map for his farm, a conservation farming guide, and information on using these tools in developing a basic conservation plan. When this additional assistance is provided, he is recorded as having an Advanced Conservation Agreement. When sufficient technical resources are available to the district, a farmer can skip over the advanced conservation agreement phase and move from his initial agreement directly to his basic conservation plan.

Under the advanced conservation agreement, the farmer is given information on the capabilities of the land and the conservation treatment it needs under alternative uses, rather than for a specific land use and farm enterprise. Technical assistance in developing a basic conservation plan is to be provided a farmer who is in the advanced conservation stage, as rapidly as possible. When it is possible, land use and treatment should be determined before technical assistance is given in the layout and application of the first permanent conservation work the farmer decides to undertake. The Washington office points out that:

. . . the first visit to the farm or ranch under the Advanced Conservation Agreement to provide technical assistance in installing permanent-type conservation work seems a logical time to assist the owner in completing his "Basic Conservation Plan."

The third stage is the completion of the basic plan, which includes three things:

(1) A decision on how the farmer is going to use and treat each field and parcel of land;
(2) Checking and discussing these decisions with the soil conservation technician;
(3) A recording of these decisions along with a statement of his intentions of what he is going to do first.

As soon as a farmer or rancher having an advanced conservation agreement definitely *determines* and *records* the specific use he will make of his land and the practices and measures he will use in conserving and improving it, he is recorded as having a Basic Conservation Plan. The basic conservation plan is no other than the traditional district farm plan.

Because of the need for a maximum of local adjustability in national conservation programming, it is imperative that the farm plan not be made to conform to any rigid national framework. For this basic block in the organization of the national program provides the means for obtaining a systematic adaptation of conservation practices to meet the local circumstances of each individual farm, without jeopardizing or lowering standards of technical adequacy. Thus, the only two national requirements for a farm conservation plan are: (1) that the farm plan be based on land capabilities as determined by soil conservation surveys; and (2) that a copy of the land capability map be included in the cooperative agreement.[24]

The land-use capabilities map is a part of the systematic procedure the Service has developed which permits the setting up of adequate technical standards within which local adaptations can be made to fit the peculiarities of each district and each farm within the district. The procedure is the classification of land according to its use capabilities,[25] and the tabulating of recommendations as to cropping systems, supporting practices, and soil treatments for each class. By January 1, 1952, detailed conservation surveys had been made of almost 400 million acres. When feasible, the districts are to be encouraged to develop and adopt land classifications and recommendations to be incorporated into their work plans.[26]

The SCS regional offices in procedural guides to their field technicians suggest that if survey data are not available so that land-use capabilities classes and treatments can be developed for immediate incorporation in the work plan, the districts should provide in their work plans for the eventual use of the land-use capabilities procedures. For example, the guide for Region III points out:

> Because the Soil Conservation Service is utilizing land-use capabilities as the basis for conservation planning, it seems desirable that the governing body include the basic concept of land-use capabilities in the work plan by recognizing that different land conditions produce

---

[24] Letter from C. L. Orrben, cited.

[25] "The classification of land according to use capabilities consists of an organized summation of physical factors — which are primarily the soil, slope, kind and degree of erosion, and climatic environment — and the interpretation of these data in terms of capability of the land." ("Classification of Land According to Use Capability," *Soil Conservation Service Manual*, No. 13730, p. 1.)

[26] "Cooperative Methods of Classifying Land," *Soil Conservation Service Manual* No. 49293, p. cont'd. 6.

different intensities of problems and require different treatment and management.[27]

The Region VI guide declares that: ". . . land-use capability classifications and recommended practices must be prepared and kept current."[28] The Service prefers that the land classes and recommendations be developed cooperatively with the various interested agencies, the district, and the local farmers. If this cooperative effort cannot be arranged, however, SCS itself takes the responsibility for developing the classifications to guide its own technicians.

The mechanism of land-use capability classes and recommended treatments makes it possible for the district to establish with more precision a floor of minimum essential practices and measures for the individual farms. When such classifications have not been developed at the writing of the district's work plan, the Service urges the districts to establish in their plans some sort of minimum technical requirements by which to judge the adequacy and acceptability of each individual farm plan as a basis for extending public assistance. In all regions, almost every district work plan gives some form of recognition to the concept of the need for certain minimum practices being established on various types of land, problem areas, and so on.

Under the new three-stage planning process, the district's establishment of a floor of minimum essential practices and measures for each class of land becomes particularly important to district maintenance of a high level of conservation standards by district farmers. For, it is believed by the national SCS office, that a majority of farmers may never arrive at a basic plan until much of the conservation work has been done on their farms. That is, conservation practices will be undertaken by the farmer on a piecemeal basis in accordance with practices recommended for each class of land in his conservation guide sheets.

The regions varyingly set up other minimum requirements as essential to an adequate farm plan. For example, Region V declares that there must be a plan of conservation operations which states *what* is to be done and *where* the specific practices are to be established. A suggested order of establishing

---

[27] "Procedure for Guidance in Cooperating with Soil Conservation Districts," *op. cit.*, p. 7.
[28] "Handbook for Farm and Ranch Conservation Planners," SCS Region VI, Memorandum No. 12 A, p. 1.

practices and a land-use map and legend are also to be included.[29] Region III, in addition to requiring the cover sheet and use capability map, explains that the following items must also be included: land-use map, plan of conservation operations, schedules of operation, cropping plans, and farm organization summary.[30]

Such specifications as these are in the nature of procedural directions to the planning technicians in the interest of making the mechanism of the plan itself technically sound, rather than an effort to pull the districts and the farmer up to any minimum level of adequacy in conservation activity. SCS also checks upon the technical quality of the planning work done by its technicians. Prior to 1942 every twenty-fifth farm plan was sent in to Washington. Since then, the zone technician working out of the regional office has had the responsibility of spot checking the technical accuracy of the farm plans. The check is made on the farm with the farmer and the planning technician.

Thus, through a series of authorizing documents and commitments, the Service is able to reach through to obtain what it considers an adequate plan of conservation operations upon the individual farm. Over the years, however, SCS has gradually de-emphasized its procedures for tieing a farmer to rigid obligations and responsibilities.

EQUIPMENT USAGE PLAN

In recent years, SCS has had so few pieces of major equipment on loan to districts, that district obligations to SCS in the use of equipment have little over-all significance in current SCS-district relations. However, an analysis of the procedure by which SCS holds districts accountable for the effective use of federal equipment aids in understanding the nature of the relationship between the districts and the federal agency. In its lending of soil conserving equipment to the districts, SCS, as a public agency, has a twofold responsibility. It has the obligation of seeing that the equipment is efficiently used in achieving the public's conservation objectives. It also has a responsibility for preventing materials purchased with public monies from being mishandled. Consequently, before the Service makes equipment available to a district, the governing body must commit itself to a further and

---

[29] *Re:* "Guide for Writing Agreements and Farm Conservation Planning," SCS Region V, Memorandum No. 433, p. 1.

[30] Memorandum from R. H. Musser, Regional Director, SCS Region III, to State Conservationists, "Farm Conservation Plans."

more specific course of action in using the equipment. That is, as a prerequisite to the granting of equipment, districts must develop suitable equipment usage plans in which they agree to handle all phases of the administration of their equipment program to the minimum extent outlined by the national office.[31]

The first purpose of such a plan is to provide for a program of operation which permits efficient use of the equipment in satisfying the conservation needs of the district. The district governing body must agree, the national office sets down as one minimum essential, to schedule the use of the equipment in the most effective manner for the advancement of the conservation program of the districts. Thus, the district is to adhere to the priority policies agreed upon in the equipment usage plan. In the model agreement provided by the national office, priorities are to be determined with consideration for the following factors:

1. The order in which requests for use of the equipment are received from cooperators.
2. Urgent need from the standpoint of necessity of establishing practices involved.
3. The availability of any required materials or other assistance to be furnished by the cooperator.
4. The location of the cooperator's farm with respect to other farms in the vicinity on which the equipment is to be operated so as to avoid excessive transportation costs.[32]

The district's original general commitment to use Service assistance only upon lands under adequate farmer-district agreement here is made specific in regard to machinery. The equipment usage plans must state that equipment will be loaned only for use on lands covered by district agreements. Moreover, the district must agree: ". . . to limit the use of Service equipment to the soil conservation program in which the Service is assisting the districts."[33]

The second purpose of the plan is to provide for the proper care by the districts of SCS equipment. The district must agree to operate the equipment only when in good operating condition. The governing body agrees to observe certain SCS regulations in the moving of equipment. The district also commits itself to

---

[31] "Equipment for Loan to Districts," *Soil Conservation Service Manual*, No. 49202, p. cont'd. 1.

[32] "Equipment Usage Plan for the ―――― Soil Conservation District," Sample Equipment Usage Plan, prepared by the Administrative Services Division, SCS.

[33] "Equipment for Loan to Districts," *op. cit.*, p. cont'd. 3.

keeping machinery in a state of good repair. Equipment is to be stored in a dry, safe place and the recommendations of the manufacturer for fueling and lubricating machinery are to be followed. Moreover, the district agrees to set up an equipment repair account for each piece of heavy machinery in operation in the district. The schedule of rates for covering repairs is to be agreed to by the district in a supplement to the equipment usage plan.

Not only is the Service interested in the districts' being financially able to repair SCS loaned equipment, but also in their building up a fund for replacing worn out SCS loaned equipment with district purchased equipment. The Service, therefore, requires that the district obligate itself in the equipment usage plan to charge farmers no less than minimum rental rates, which adequately cover fixed charges, operating costs, salaries and wages, major repair fund, equipment amortization fund, transportation, and contingent costs.[34]

Whereas the national office merely requires that minimum rates be sufficient to cover the cost of operation, repair, and amortization of machinery, the regional offices put the rates on a dollar and cents basis. In 1946, the House Appropriations Subcommittee on Agriculture closely questioned the assistant chief of SCS on the extent to which the Service had made provision for the districts' building up an adequate replacement fund. This nicely illustrates how the public, through its national legislative representatives, holds the Service rather than the districts accountable for the suitable use of federal equipment.[35]

In its effort to insure that the districts carry out the provisions of their equipment operation plans, the Service makes two further requirements. The responsibility for managing Service loaned equipment is to be isolated in one or more individuals, specifically charged with particular equipment responsibilities. The Service is to have ample opportunity for keeping informed on how the district is actually managing and caring for its equipment. The district agrees to keep records of all work performed by the equipment, repairs and inspections made, funds collected and bills paid in connection with operation and transportation of the equipment. SCS personnel are always to have access to the equipment, and may inspect it at any time. The national

---

[34] "Equipment Usage Plan for ———— Soil Conservation District," *op. cit.,* pp. 4, 5. *See also* "Equipment for Loan to Districts," *op. cit.,* p. cont'd.

[35] House Appropriation *Hearings,* 1947, *op. cit.,* p. 1057.

office specifically states that any deviations from the minimum essentials it lays down for an equipment operation plan: ". . . must have the prior approval of the Regional Conservator."[36]

Service Disinclination To Use Coercion

Through this progressive gearing together of formal SCS-district agreements and district policy documents, each district is committed to a framework of minimum obligations which Service officials see as necessary for an acceptable basis for extending SCS assistance. Charges are frequently made that the procedures the district must follow are so rigid that local people cannot change anything but the minute details of the SCS program, or that supervisors are so circumscribed by SCS standards, standardized procedures, and forms that they have little room for exercising any discretion in their district program. Although there are elements of reality in these charges, they are not substantiated by the Service's use of its coercive power. As in the traditional grant-in-aid relationships, the federal agency has been most reluctant to use coercive measures either in establishing the original framework of specific district obligations or in keeping the districts to their commitments.

According to the authorizing agreements, the Service is progressively to commit itself to making assistance available to a district only as the district progressively develops and commits itself to administrative policies judged by SCS regional offices to be adequate for carrying on an effective conservation program. Yet never has the Service found it expedient to refuse to enter into a cooperative relationship with a district because of inability of SCS and the district to agree upon suitable district working processes. Region IV has declared that:

. . . an adequate program and plan are absolutely necessary if we are to avoid inefficiencies and waste of public funds. If the plan is not adequate and we sign a Supplemental Memorandum with a district, we commit ourselves to an inadequacy. We can be bound to it. As servants of the people, we have a continuing and enduring responsibility to accomplish permanent conservation for the largest number of acres and people.[37]

Even Region IV, however, after rejecting a certain district's work plan several times, finally accepted it as a basis for coop-

---

[36] "Equipment Operation Plan," *Soil Conservation Service Manual,* No. 49202.1, p. cont'd.

[37] "District Programs and Work Plans as an Adequate Basis for Service Assistance," Region IV, *op. cit.,* p. 3.

eration when the district board at last issued an ultimatum: "Here it is, accept it or not."

Regional offices seldom find any work plan submitted for their approval so inadequate that it must be returned to a district for redrafting to conform to Service policies. The very pointing out of the fact that one regional office has on occasions called for the prior submission of rough drafts and has red-penciled district work plans testifies to such practices being the noteworthy exceptions. This does not mean, however, that regional offices do not generally obtain the inclusion of all the policies and procedures they believe necessary for adequate district performance of conservation work. Usually the technicians, clearly instructed in the regional office's requirements in a work plan, can be depended upon to guide the new and inexperienced supervisors into preparing work plans that will be acceptable to the regional office.

So reluctant are the regional offices to turn down a work plan submitted by a district that if state and district personnel do not succeed in getting the district's adoption of an adequate plan, the regional office generally accepts the inadequate one. In such cases, however, official displeasure clearly falls upon the field personnel who have permitted the regional office to be put in the embarrassing position of having to accept an unsuitable plan. In short, although the regional offices do have the authority to require districts to commit themselves to certain administrative policies, as a condition to extending assistance, most of the regions have not established fixed minimum requirements which must be met. Moreover, they have generally been most hesitant to use even the threat of non-cooperation to persuade a district to revise a work plan submitted to the regional office.

The fact that district governing bodies have generally accepted the guidance of SCS field personnel in drafting their official administrative policies does not mean that supervisors are, in reality, being limited in their freedom to determine district policies; for the provisions of the district program and work plans are not regarded as binding commitments either by the district boards or by the Service. So little consideration have district boards given their original formal policy documents that frequently supervisors do not readily recall such documents when they are mentioned. It is generally agreed that in a preponderance of districts the work plan is not used by the district board as a guide in its administrative decisions.

The Service, for its part, has not found it expedient meticulously to keep boards to their official commitments as the price for Service assistance. The Service has, of course, the right to abrogate its supplemental memorandum with a district, withdraw its technical personnel assisting a district, or withdraw the machinery it has loaned a district, if a district does not live up to its commitments. Yet, the Service has never cancelled a supplemental memorandum with a district or withdrawn its technical services from a district because of a governing board's failure to comply with its written obligations. The only supplemental memorandum that has ever been cancelled with a district was at one grazing district's official request, when the district discovered that it was not to receive the federal marginal lands which seemingly had been the sole local incentive for organizing a district.

So reluctant has the Service been to cancel a memorandum that it has not cancelled memoranda with a number of almost dormant districts. Nor has SCS ever withdrawn all its technical personnel from a district even when the district board's failure to comply with its formally agreed upon policies was so flagrant that it was obvious that the supervisors had no interest at all in accomplishing conservation.

Experience with one district in the Southwest is a case in point. Not only did the supervisors of this particular district have no appreciation of their positions as public servants and no interest in conservation, but they were even dishonest. Over the protests of the technicians, the supervisors insisted on the district's taking on only those jobs which would show a neat profit. Then, at the end of the year, they counted up the profits, divided them by five, and wrote checks to themselves for their equal shares. Although the supervisors were incensed when the SCS technician objected to this procedure, they were sufficiently uneasy that they never cashed the checks. Although SCS was completely disgusted with its every experience with this district, it did not discontinue its work unit until the supervisors asked the technicians to leave at the beginning of the war, when the board officially decided that the government should not be wasting its money on conservation. Moreover, the supplemental memorandum with the district never having been cancelled, working relations have been reestablished since the war.

The only cause of SCS personnel's voluntarily "pulling out" of a district has been such a lack of local interest in conservation that the farm planners do not have enough work to keep them fully occupied. And even these withdrawals are quite rare. In these cases, only the farm planners were removed. The services of the district conservationist were still available to the districts. Of course, the number of SCS personnel within a district is frequently changed in the Service's effort to equalize the farm planning work loads among the technicians.

Because of the Service's limited number of professional field workers, technical assistance should probably also be removed when the policies of a district board towards cooperating farmers are such that no adequate or permanent erosion control is being accomplished. That SCS officials realize the advisability of such withdrawals is reflected by a memorandum from the Region VI director to his field staff. He points out the field personnel's responsibility to advise a board on its duty to deny district assistance to farmers unwilling to perform a minimum of essential practices:

> The achievement of a satisfactory amount of conservation for every dollar spent by the Service is of extreme importance at this particular time. The Service is facing a period ahead (perhaps the beginning of the new fiscal year) when increased funds and other resources will be less abundant than has been the case in the past. We must prepare for this time in every way possible. Included in these preparations will be Service effort to shift resources whenever necessary from places of low conservation accomplishment (due to non-acceptance of program) to those places where the most conservation is being gotten for the money expended. We are not ignoring soil decline classifications in making the decision — as a matter of fact in areas where deterioration of land and water resources is acute we may be in position to give more assistance as a result of this action. In every case, however, where further progress seems stymied for the time being on some part of the district program, I am sure everyone will agree that it is good business to shift Service resources to other locations.[38]

Because loaned machinery is constantly being withdrawn from districts as a district's use for it diminishes or another district's needs become relatively greater, the Service seldom makes an issue of withdrawing equipment because of its being mishandled by a district. Moreover, the threat of withdrawal of equipment is to be used only sparingly. Equipment "inspections should not be made to appear," the Region III office instructs its field staff, ". . . that they are to find fault with how the district

---

[38] "Technical Assistance in Questionable Cases — Suggestions to District Supervisors," SCS Region VI, Memorandum No. 37, from Cyril Luker, Regional Conservator, to State and District Conservationists, March 20, 1947, p. 2.

is taking care of equipment, but as something that furnishes information as to what is needed to keep equipment in safe and efficient operating condition."[39] The Service relies primarily upon the good offices of its field men working with the supervisors to obtain a district's compliance with its equipment usage plan.

Service reluctance to withdraw equipment because of its misuse by a district is illustrated in its experience with a wind erosion district. The county governing body, the legal administrator of the wind erosion district, looking upon the district as another patronage device, insisted on awarding the job of operating SCS loaned equipment on a political basis. As long as the operator chosen was capable and honest, SCS was willing to go along with the county. Even when the county chose a one-handed operator, who was disadvantaged in handling heavy equipment, SCS employees accepted the county's choice. When Service personnel later confronted the county with evidence of the operator's inefficiency and his dishonesty in making his time reports, the county would approve no other operator. Finally, as a last resort, the Service found it necessary to threaten to remove its machinery from the district before the county agreed to another operator.

To summarize the federal effort to establish a framework for Service-district relationships: In the first place, the organizational documents and agreements, which had the element of coercion behind them, rather than limiting local initiative and responsibility, were attempting to commit the districts to certain acts of specific performance. Secondly, although SCS has the coercive power of withholding and withdrawing federal assistance until districts conform to certain minimum administrative policies, local determination of district policies has not been thwarted through Service use of these coercive measures.

If the districts have been merely tools of the Soil Conservation Service in carrying out a nationally determined local program, if there has been little local determination of district policies, the constraining force has not been district commitments in formal agreements to fixed standards and procedures. Rather it is in the operating relationships between the supervisors and the Service technicians as the work of the district gets under way. The Service is depending upon its technicians, who are given specific central directions, to obtain district conformance to adequate

---

[39] "Procedure for Guidance in Cooperating with Soil Conservation Districts," *op. cit.*, pp. 26, 27.

conservation operations through their day-to-day work in the district. It is in the operational balancing of the institutional personalities of farmer supervisors and Service technicians — in the weight of their respective competencies, energies, and will to make the district effective — that the pattern of district administration is formed. Whether it is to be technician administration, or farmer supervisor administration which blends into itself the knowledge and experience of its technical assistants, is dependent upon daily working relationships.

CHAPTER 4

Role of District Supervisors

An integral part of the effort to balance national programming with local government is the exercising of such local determination by farm people themselves rather than by the local representatives of the Soil Conservation Service. Although a farmer governing body must properly be responsible for developing and administering the soil conservation program in the district, it is unrealistic and out of harmony with the whole district philosophy to assume the complete separateness of the Service technician's responsibilities from those of the supervisors. The technician's function of giving technical guidance in the application of conservation practices cannot and perhaps should not be compartmentalized and completely isolated from the supervisor's function of managing the district. These two responsibilities are interwoven in the functioning of the district. A constructive blending of the special knowledge and experiences of both farmers and technicians in arriving at conservation judgments is needed.

Thus far in district administration the tendency has been for farmer supervisors to shift too large a share of their work in managing the district to the Service technicians. SCS field personnel, well equipped with technical knowledge in conservation and working on a full-time paid basis, are anxious to show satisfactory conservation accomplishments to administrative superiors. In contrast, farmer supervisors, new and inexperienced in the scientific techniques of soil conservation, are busy making a living elsewhere and often are carrying other time-consuming organized group and community responsibilities.

In analyzing the relationships between supervisors and district technicians, it is not sufficient to estimate that a certain number of district governing bodies are very active, fairly active, or inactive in carrying on their functions. Rather, each activity in the administrative process requires examination to discover what can and should be expected of district supervisors, and how technical advice and assistance can be utilized without sacrificing farmer supervisor control over district affairs.

VARYING VIEWS OF SUPERVISOR'S JOB

During the years in which the district has been in operation, four general responsibilities of the farmer governing body have emerged. One SCS regional director sums these up as: (1) enlisting the technical skills and services of various federal, state and local agencies that can contribute effectively to the advancement of their programs for better land use and soil conservation; (2) bringing together local forces — community leaders, civic organizations, business and educational institutions, and other individuals or groups — who separately or collectively can assist in rendering direct assistance to the district; (3) promoting and selling conservation to farm operators within the districts; and (4) governing the district.

Although the supervisors' functions in selling conservation to farmers and in bringing together local forces are of great importance to the successful operation of the district, the critical question is: what is the governing function of district supervisors? There are two varying, but reconcilable, concepts of the role of the supervisors in governing the district.

The first is generally empirical and unexpressed. It is the view of supervisors as primarily a combination of "extra hands" for SCS personnel, and political buffers between technicians and farmers and community groups. It grows out of the Service's dependence upon its district staffs to obtain district pursuance of administrative policies which "agree fundamentally with the principles of the assisting Service." Although the supervisors are to make district decisions, district SCS workers, in their responsibility for the board's making the "right" decision, often feel that they must shape the district policies which the supervisors officially adopt. For example, the directives sent by one of the SCS regional offices to its work unit staffs have rested upon no other assumption than that SCS personnel is actually making district policies.

In substance, district supervisors are to be extra hands for the Service technicians. The supervisors are to bring in applications for farm plans. They are to arrange for educational and other types of group meetings. They are to solicit assistance from a variety of local groups. They are to iron out difficulties between individual farmers and technicians. In addition, they are to perform all of the routine administrative tasks of the district — such as approving applications, reviewing farm plans, keeping records and accounts, issuing planting stock, seeing to routing and upkeep of machinery, and so on. Often the degree to which supervisors are governing their districts is estimated by their acceptance of such busy work.

In contrast, the district governing body sometimes is viewed as a purely policy determining or judicial body, removed from any routine administrative responsibilities. Supervisors themselves often express this view of their job. District conservationists and farm planners in all sections of the country report that farmers are inclined to feel that the technicians should carry on the routine administrative work of the district. Repeatedly, supervisors are described as — shirking detail work, feeling themselves too busy to carry on the routine jobs of the district, and envisioning their function as simply that of meeting to approve or disapprove plans and reports prepared by the technicians. It is not unusual for supervisors to see their job as similar to that of directors of a bank.

A third view holds that if district governing bodies are, in fact, to govern their districts, they must be both a policy determining body and an administrative body which carries on the routine management activities of the districts. It is generally agreed that the governing body is properly the group which initiates, checks, and controls district policies. But the routine activities in managing the district also are properly those of the supervisors or their chosen local representatives. A policy determining body which does not have operational responsibilities and duties often does not, in reality, exercise its policy functions. The policies which actually guide an administrative operation are generally the accumulation of small operational decisions. Only through experience with the day-to-day operation of the district can supervisors gain the knowledge in conservation activity which will equip them for making policy decisions. Without such experience and knowledge, farmers also are generally reluctant to take the responsibility of decision-making.

In terms of conservation accomplishment, it is wasteful to use the limited number of technically trained men to perform the routine administrative work of the district. As pointed out by the New York State conservationist, in an annual meeting of New York soil conservation directors:

Last year's accomplishments were rather low — too low, in fact, to keep pace with present losses of soil. They do not represent the maximum use to which SCS technicians can be put. . . . One reason that the SCS may not have accomplished more was the requests made of the technicians by the Directors [supervisors] to do work which is not the responsibility of technical men. . . .

What, then, are the policy decisions involved in carrying conservation to the lands of each farmer in a district? What policy decisions must supervisors make if they are, in fact, to govern the district? To what extent are supervisors generally making such decisions? What administrative activities must supervisors or a district-employed staff perform, if the governing body is actually to initiate, supervise, and control conservation activity? To what extent should technicians advise and guide governing bodies in carrying on each of these activities, in the interest of maintaining minimum standards of adequacy in conservation treatments, and economy and efficiency in the operation of the district administration?

SUPERVISORS AS POLICY-MAKERS

The process of administering any collective activity usually breaks down into policy formulation and determination, policy execution, and the checking and control of the execution of policy. In the confusion of reality, there are no clear-cut stages in a total administrative process. The total administrative job is made up of a series of interrelated activities which are, at any one time, at varying stages in the process of administration. Even within one rather narrow activity all stages of administration are being carried on simultaneously. Finally, the activities themselves intertwine to compose the total activity. But for the convenience of analysis, the administrative process of a conservation district must be artificially broken down into operational stages and into various types of operating activities.

Policy formulation and determination in any collective activity commonly involves the development of two general types of policies, substantive and procedural. In a conservation district, the establishment of substantive policies consists of setting up major conservation goals, emphases, and practices of the district, and the defining of the relationship between farmer cooperators and the district in reaching these goals. Developing procedural policies involves the establishment of organizational arrangements and working processes for carrying the substantive policies into effect.

It is in the determination of what the nature of the district's conservation program is to be that farmer judgments are probably of greatest value. The Soil Conservation Service, in cooperation with the state experiment stations, has worked out the technical combinations of conservation measures and practices which are necessary for treating each of a series of land classes. SCS technicians are equipped to survey and classify accurately and quickly the rural lands of each district. Thus, the Service is technically capable of telling farmers of a district what conservation activities must be carried out if they are adequately to preserve their soil; what the major conservation emphasis of the district should properly be; what minimum conservation treatments should be insisted upon for each class of land; what commitments and obligations the farmer cooperators should properly assume.

In short, the Service staff can probably develop the technically "best" conservation program for any district in the United States. Yet, such a program might not be well suited to the district for which it was specifically designed. This might be the case if the reactions of local farm people, who were being depended upon to carry out the district program, were miscalculated. Farmer supervisors often are characterized by SCS field personnel as being better equipped than Service technicians to judge the palatability of proposed district conservation policies in terms of the habits, attitudes, and desires of the district's farm people.

Marking Out Major Emphasis for District Activity

The conservation accomplishments of a district depend upon the will of local farmers to expend labor and resources on carrying out conservation work on their lands. Therefore, it is of prime importance for the district to catch local opinion as to what are the most pressing conservation problems, to estimate probable farmer attitudes towards attempting certain types of practices, and to appreciate the degree to which farmers will attempt to adjust their farm operations to the best land-use capabilities plan.

Farmer supervisors are probably in the best position to determine, in the light of local attitudes, what the major emphasis of the conservation program should be at various stages in the development of the district. Farmer governing bodies have made this single policy decision more commonly than any other decision. A preponderance of districts have received their organization impetus from the real need or desire of local people to accomplish one particular conservation job. Farmer supervisors have reflected the local desire which led to the creation of the district in determining the original major emphasis of the program. For example, Leake District, Mississippi, has emphasized the drainage of more level lands, so that the steeper slopes may be retired from cultivation. Improving irrigation practices has been a large part of the program of San Mateo District, California. The Winooski District, Vermont, originally concentrated on stream bank erosion control.

After a district has been cooperating with farmers in conservation work over a period of time, farmer supervisors have been active in pushing particular practices which have proved popular with the farmers of their district. For example, supervisors have reflected the appeal that the farm pond program has had for farmers by pushing this type of conservation work in many districts. In many southern districts, such as Holmes County, Mississippi, growing farmer awareness of the need for more and better pastures has resulted in supervisors' taking the lead in shifting the emphasis of their district's program to developing better pasturage.

Setting Minimum Conservation Obligations for Farmer Cooperators

In all sections of the country, district conservationists and farm planners predominantly point out that the determination of the major emphases of the conservation program is one of the fundamental policy decisions which should be and is being made by district supervisors. Yet, the contrasting experience and background attitudes of the Service staff and farmer supervisors have made for a conflict of opinion in this primary policy area.

COMPLETE FARM PLAN

Farmer supervisors are keenly responsive to local opinions as to the most pressing conservation needs of the district. Consequently not sufficiently convinced of the need for rounded conservation activity, they have frequently wished to concentrate district resources largely upon one or more of the popular practices. They have not readily seen the necessity for obligating a farmer to carry through a complete conservation program upon his land when his only interest is in accomplishing one particular conservation job. The experience of one Utah district typifies this problem. Because of widespread farmer interest in land leveling, supervisors were furnishing district technical engineering assistance to farmers to carry out this one particular job. Even after several months, no complete farm plans had been written for the farmers who were given this assistance.

The staff of the Soil Conservation Service, with a technical perception of the need for the employment of adequate combinations of conservation practices upon each acre of a farm, believes that the conservation program of a district must encompass all necessary soil conserving practices. In short, the supervisors and the Service staff have had varying concepts of what the district's relationships to cooperating farmers should be.

The Service originally believed that for the effective saving of the soil of a district, each farmer who received district assistance should be committed to carrying out a rounded conservation program — that is, that the farmer had to accept a complete farm plan. Supervisors, on the other hand, had to be educated in the necessity for the district's giving on-site assistance only to a farmer who agreed to a complete farm plan which provided for certain minimum essential practices. All district boards formally accepted the Service dictum that there had to be a farmer-district agreement in which the farmer accepted a complete farm plan. But supervisor modification of this policy was reflected in the frequency with which SCS farm planners "bootlegged" on-site assistance to farmers who had no plan. The various ways in which the Service had relaxed its policy of the complete farm plan even before April, 1951, is telling testimony of farmer supervisors' real influence in this policy field.[1]

MINIMUM ESSENTIAL PRACTICES

A part of the concept of the complete farm plan is the establishment of minimum combinations of conservation practices necessary for the adequate preservation of each class of land. Supervisors, of course, have the legal authority to determine at what level of technical adequacy such minimums should be set, or if a district policy on minimum practices is to be established at all. The Service prefers that the governing bodies set up such minimums in their work plans, so that the SCS farm planner will have the support of official district policy in urging a farmer to accept practices necessary for his doing a sound conservation job on his farm. Farmer governing bodies usually exercise little initiative in the formulation of the minimum policies which are incorporated in the original work plan of a district.[2]

---

[1] For fuller discussion of this trend in Service policy, see Chapter 6.
[2] For fuller discussion of this point, see pages 94–96.

The real policy decisions on what the minimum conservation practices upon farms must be are made in the day-to-day operation of the district. Before the establishment of the three-stage planning procedure, in 1951, such decisions were made in the preparation, review, and acceptance of each farm plan. In working out a conservation plan with a farmer, the farm planner, as an SCS employee, had the duty of urging the farmer to agree to carrying out a maximum of desirable conservation practices. The farmer, of course, was completely free to accept or reject the technician's suggestions. The technician was to write the plan which the farmer was willing to agree to carry out. Whether or not the plan was approved as an acceptable basis for rendering district assistance to the farmer was to be the decision of the governing body in each particular case. If the supervisors gave a real review to each farm plan and made a decision as to the adequacy of those plans the technicians considered questionable, then, in the accumulation of such single decisions, farmer supervisors were actually determining district policy on minimum practices.

The Service felt that, because the assistance it had available for the district was numerically insufficient to meet the conservation needs of the nation, its field staff had a duty to push for the district's acceptance of only those farm plans which would bring about some real conservation accomplishment. The SCS director in Region VI pointed out this duty to his field staff:

> It may be that the board is not in sympathy with the Service viewpoint on the particular case. This calls for logical thinking and painstaking effort on the part of the district conservationist to explain to and convince the board members that continued cooperation under existing conditions can only result in eventual embarrassment and impairment of the district program. If a good presentation is made, the board will see the logic of the case and accept the entire responsibility for denying assistance. On such occasions, the district conservationist is the Service's representative and he must stand fully behind Service principles.[3]

Even so, because the success of such a voluntary program of conservation is so dependent upon farmer good will and desire to work with the districts, the supervisors had the important role of interpreting local attitudes and reactions to determine what the traffic would bear in the way of district insistence on the acceptance of certain minimum practices. Moreover, SCS was usually willing

---

[3] "Technical Assistance in Questionable Cases — Suggestions to District Supervisors," *op cit.,* p. 2.

to accept the decisions of the governing body on this issue, as it always is loathe to "pull out" of any district.

The district conservationist, whose success in a district is usually judged in the state SCS office by his ability to work well with the district supervisors, seldom takes issue with the supervisors whenever they see fit to reject the technician's opinions. As a matter of record, when a district conservationist or farm planner and the governing body have not been able to agree upon the operations of a district, the Service has generally undertaken to replace its employee with one more agreeable to the governing body.[4]

Despite the fact that a farmer can now become a district co-operator and receive district assistance before he has a complete conservation plan, the concept of minimum essential practices for adequate conservation accomplishment has not been abandoned. The conservation guide which a farmer receives, as he goes into the advanced planning stage, attempts to set a high level for conservation performance in its outline of the alternative uses that can safely be made for each of the classes of land on his farm and the conservation measures required for adquate treatment.

In all regions, state and district conservationists are laying stress upon the need for getting supervisors actively to participate in the preparation of conservation guide sheets for their district. District supervisors, SCS feels, can aid technicians in determining the highest level of conservation standards which will be acceptable to the farmers of their district. Although a farmer need no longer commit himself to a particular plan of conservation operations for his farm before he receives district assistance, SCS is now officially convinced of the rightness of the long-held supervisor opinion that a farmer who has been given a taste of the advantages of conservation, through district assistance in the installation of a particular conservation measure, will eventually accept a more adequate complete plan than will a farmer who is pressed to accept a complete farm plan before he has tried conservation farming.

DISTRIBUTION OF PLANTING STOCK

Supervisors also face a series of decisions concerning the furnishing of materials to cooperating farmers. Is the district to attempt to get planting stock, in addition to that supplied by the Service, to distribute to its cooperators? On what basis should

---

[4] *See* pages 104, 105.

available materials be allotted to farmers? Generally, Service workers have largely determined how the materials SCS makes available to the district are to be distributed. Often the proportions of planting stock the farmer and the districts are to provide are written into the farm plan, and materials are then distributed by the technicians as called for in the plans. That supervisors are typically prone not to see the need for distinguishing too categorically between cooperating and non-cooperating farmers in the distribution of soil conserving stocks is illustrated by the supervisors of the Tygart's Valley District, West Virginia. They believed that lime from the lime plant, which the district was planning to establish, should be available to all farmers of the area, irrespective of their status with the district.[5]

In numerous districts, supervisors have felt it necessary to obtain more planting materials for district farmers than those made available by the Service. For example, the Eastern Colfax District, New Mexico, was successful in winning over to its conservation program landowners who were formerly bitterly opposed, by buying and distributing over 20,000 pounds of crested wheat grass.

To give a few illustrations to show how districts, within the course of a year, acted to secure planting stock for their cooperators without the material assistance of the Service: Twenty Kansas districts purchased grass seed. In Oklahoma, several districts provided at least 15,000 pounds of native grass seed for the use of their cooperators. Eight districts in Northwest Florida purchased more than 30,000 pounds of Dixie Crimson Clover seed for distribution among cooperators. In Alabama nearly a million kudzu crowns were grown by individual farmers for use in the district's program.

USE OF COERCION BY DISTRICT

Perhaps the most important policy decision which the supervisors have made in determining farmer-district relationships has been their expressed or tacit unwillingness to push for the use of district land-use regulations — that is, the use of police power to force non-cooperating farmers to carry out certain conservation measures. Here again the supervisors have acted as weathervanes, usually correctly registering what local farmer reaction would be

---

[5] Unless otherwise indicated, the following information on district supervisors' activities is taken from interviews with district supervisors and SCS field personnel, district annual reports, state conservationist reports, and minutes of district supervisors association meetings.

to the adoption of compulsory land-use regulations. The original misreading of farmer opinion by the supervisors of Southside District, Virginia, in 1942, nicely illustrates the utility of supervisors in gauging farmer attitudes. The supervisors explain in their 1943 annual report:

> There is one statement in our report of last year that we wish to recant. We quote from the 1942 report: "We believe the Supervisors are willing to take the first steps toward compulsory conservation." We may be willing to take such steps at some time in the future in this direction, but feel that there is a growing resentment at present toward all compulsion and feel that any steps in this direction now might do more harm than good.

Farmer supervisors also are making other policy decisions concerning farmer relationships with the district. Governing bodies have ordinarily accepted the form suggested by the Service for district-farmer agreements, which spelled out the farmer's obligation to complete his conservation plan. Nevertheless, they have still determined district policy upon farmer obligations to the district. Despite the damage-liability provision in many of the old agreement forms, supervisors have viewed the farmer agreements only as gentlemen's agreements not to be enforced by law. The SCS Washington office knows of no district which has attempted to recover the cost of assistance or materials it has made available to a farmer who has not complied with his agreement.

Establishing Working Priorities

One of the large groups of policy decisions involved in developing the procedural arrangements for carrying on the work of the district is in the establishment of a series of priority policies. Priorities must be set up for accepting farmer applications, providing farmers with technical assistance in planning, and applying conservation treatment to their lands. Basic in determining priorities for assisting farmers is the decision on the administrative method to be used in carrying conservation planning and assistance in application to farmers. This is largely the question of whether conservation planning and instructions in applying some of the practices are to be carried out on a group or individual basis.

If the decision is to plan on a group basis, what is to be the area for group activity — the natural neighborhood or community, a small watershed, or some other type of group? How are priorities among groups to be established — on the basis of the urgency of the need for soil conservation work, or the degree of farmer interest within the area? What criteria are to be used to determine a priority schedule for servicing individual farmers within the group — a farmer's interest alone or also his ability to contribute adequate labor and material in the conservation treatment of his farm? How is farmer interest to be measured? If planning and application are to be done on an individual basis, how are work priorities to be determined — on the basis of time order of application for assistance? the demonstrational value of the farm as a conservation farm? the need of the farmer for controlling his land's erosion? or convenience and economy in terms of traveling time for technicians assisting the farmer and in moving conservation equipment?

POTENTIALITIES IN FARMER SUPERVISOR JUDGMENTS

The staff of the Soil Conservation Service, in view of the magnitude of the conservation job and its limited personnel, has felt the need for devising a method of conservation planning and application which permits each technician to assist a greater number of farmers than he has been able to serve on the individual basis. Thus, it presses for the adoption of the group approach in all districts. Farmer supervisors, on the other hand, must be educated to the value of the group approach in planning. If left without guidance in deciding the order in which farmers should receive assistance, the average board would probably follow the procedure which a supervisor from the Valley County District, Nebraska, described at the Nebraska Supervisors' Fifth State Conference:

> We have everybody come in a rotation as they apply for their work. We don't jump around any more than we have to. We divide it as close as we can and not run the outfit all over the county.[6]

Perhaps the exigencies of the conservation task demand the increasing use of the group approach by the districts. Yet, the very fact that farmer supervisors have a background experience differing from that of the Service staff has made it wise also to utilize farmer experience in determining the criteria for establishing priorities and for making priority decisions upon the order of district assistance to farmers. Farmers have shown a fund of perti-

---

[6] Proceedings, Nebraska's Fifth State Soil Conservation District Supervisors' Conference, Lincoln, January 16, 17, 1946, p. 21.

nent local knowledge for judging the utility of the group approach.

Supervisors frequently know whether the social or community habits of the farmers of their area will permit them to work effectively in groups. For example, district supervisors in Colorado have questioned the suitability of the group approach in their districts because of the newness and fluidity of their communities. They do not believe that their neighbors have yet developed that local social cohesiveness which facilitates their working well together in groups. Supervisors often perceive that the farmers of their acquaintance will not accept the necessity for being in a group as a just basis for determining eligibility for conservation assistance. For example, the supervisors of a Mississippi district noted in one of their annual reports that some of the:

> . . . landowners have objected to group planning. These few farmers say that they do not think it is fair to withhold the available assistance from them just because their neighbors are backward and do not want to improve their farms.

Iowa district commissioners, in a 1950 state meeting, questioned the fairness and efficacy of ignoring the interest and willingness of the individual farmer in determining the order in which farmers are to receive technical assistance.

Supervisors sometimes appreciate that the local farmers are generally not sufficiently oriented in scientific farming to have the capacity to go ahead with conservation treatments without a maximum of individual guidance. For example, the supervisors of a Georgia district report:

> The average cooperator seems unable or unwilling to go very far toward changing from established habits to new and better methods of soil management without a lot of personal supervision and guidance.

Supervisors of one North Dakota district, after a few trial group meetings, reported that they were:

> . . . very strongly of the opinion that for the present any educational work designed to train farmers to work out their own soil and water conservation practices would be of too technical a nature for farmers in that area.

Farmer supervisors often believe that effort spent in group meetings represents a loss of time in getting practices applied, since farmer cooperators will still require as much individual attention as without the group instruction. This was the supervisor reaction to the experience with group planning in one Mississippi district:

> Since our last report we have held group meetings of our farmers to arrange for planning and especially for mapping of farms adjoining or adjacent to each other. A few such meetings were successful, the balance accomplished very little. The commissioners are convinced that the farmers do not attend these meetings because they do not understand the program, and that such farmers need the aid of the Service far more than the farmers who do attend. Also, that every farmer must have agricultural aid on his own farm hillside or in his own gully to advise him before the thinking gets clear. . . . Nothing can substitute for personal contact.

This supervisor objection to the use of the group approach has, according to SCS officials, largely lost its validity in the three-stage planning process. Equipped with the conservation guide sheets which districts are now preparing to go along with farm land-use capability maps, farmers, working in their neighborhood groups, can carry on a great deal of conservation work without special on-site assistance.

If the supervisors do accept the group approach as the most efficient way of spreading conservation activity, they frequently have knowledge of which groups of farmers can productively work together. For instance, they may realize that the men who farm the lands of a small watershed are socially incompatible for working together as a conservation group. Or if the natural neighborhood or community is chosen as the working group, supervisors often aid in the bounding of such social areas.

In determining priorities for the planning of farms on an individual basis, the supervisors have understood their community well enough to know what will be considered equitable and practical bases for determining the order of assistance. When spotting conservation farms throughout a district for their demonstrational value, supervisors frequently have pointed out that the conservation treatment of certain farms, although not strategically located geographically, would have considerable selling power because of the personality or leadership qualities of the farmer.

FARMER SUPERVISOR ACTIVITY IN PRIORITY DECISIONS

Farmer supervisors, although they have the capacity to contribute to the making of priority decisions, have not yet completely appreciated the need for establishing priority policies.

Consequently they are not yet sufficiently utilizing their authority in this policy area. This is reflected in three or four patterns in district priority decisions.

The lack of supervisor participation in determining the methods and priorities for spreading conservation work is reflected, first, in the geographical pattern of district use of the group approach in conservation planning and application. Before the national SCS office began strongly urging regional and state SCS offices to convince district boards of the necessity for group planning, the districts using the group approach were clustered within certain regions and states. This indicated that the decision for a district to carry on its conservation activity upon a group basis was essentially that of Service personnel at the regional or state level rather than of farmer supervisors.

Region IV instructions on "Developing a Work Unit Annual Plan of Operations" reveal that the regional office made no other assumption than that planning in all districts would be on a group basis. In determining the conservation job for the next year, the work unit was to:

a. Train all Professional and SP-6 employees to conduct group application meetings, and assign them the responsibility of conducting meetings.
b. Conservation group Meetings will be held seasonally. Usually two meetings each year will be sufficient in most districts. . . .
c. "On the Ground Method Application" meetings will be held seasonally to give training on techniques on applying conservation practices. . . .
d. Adequate preparation will be made prior to each meeting.

This preparation will include at least the following:

(1) Analyses of practices planned and applied by the group
(2) Contacting group leaders or key farmers and ranchers to arrange for meetings
(3) Contacting all members of group if necessary to get attendance at first meeting if other methods have failed

On-site assistance. . .

b. On-site technical assistance will be scheduled to individual farms on basis of conservation needs and farmer intention lists. (Should have originated at group application meetings.)
c. Assistance to farmers who did not attend meetings or those not in conservation groups will be scheduled only after assistance scheduled at group meetings has been given.

Not only have the districts in this region almost unanimously insisted on the exclusive use of the group approach, but they have determined a farmer's eligibility for assistance by his attendance of group meetings. To quote from the work plan of the Mason County District, Texas, as an illustration:

> The Board of Supervisors feel that more work can be done and better plans made by working with groups rather than individuals. It will be the policy of this Board to work with groups; these groups to be known as conservation groups. . . . As a minimum limit, it will be the policy to approve a group of five men, who must be adjacent or closely grouped, or an acreage of 3,000 acres, whichever is the smaller. This does not mean that this is the desired size of group; but it is the minimum. . . .
>
> A few requests will be approved on farms or ranches, as examples, in sections where it is not possible to organize conservation groups because of lack of interest or other reasons. These will be for the purpose of demonstrating to neighboring farmers and ranchers what the District proposes to do and will be approved only after organization of conservation groups has failed. . . .
>
> Two types of meetings will be held with groups of landowners prior to planning their farms or ranches with them. One meeting will be an educational meeting to acquaint them with the District. . . . The other type of meeting will be a planning meeting covering the details of working out a conservation plan covering the items listed above. . . .
>
> For a landowner to receive District assistance he or his represent-ative must attend one or both of the meetings. If he is unable to attend either meeting but shows that he received the information given in the meeting from someone who did attend, either the supervisors or their representatives, he will be given District assistance.

In contrast to the relatively long established uniform district pattern of group planning in Region IV, the pronounced nation-wide swing to the group approach did not set in until 1946. Clearly the nation-wide district shift to the group approach was the result of pressure from the national SCS office rather than the fortuitous accumulation of local decisions independently arrived at by farmer supervisors. As Congress, holding the Soil Conser-vation Service rather than the local districts accountable for the rate of conservation accomplishment, increased its insistence that SCS speed up the work of getting conservation on the land, the national SCS office increasingly has exerted pressure on the districts to adopt the group approach as a means of maximizing the number of farmers the SCS technicians could assist.

A letter from H. H. Bennett to all Service personnel in August, 1948, indicates the strong drive the national office has been making since that time for the adoption of the group approach:

Fig. 6 — Farm ponds like this one in Ohio have been a popular practice with district supervisors.

Fig. 7 — A dam with tile drain protects the gully, and the shoreline and dam in this farm pond are protected by aquatic vegetation.

With each passing month, the need for speeding up and improving the quality of soil- and water-conservation work becomes more important. . . . These facts require that the Soil Conservation Service take every possible appropriate step that will help it, and the soil-conservation districts of the country do the best possible job of conserving the Nation's remaining soil and water resources. . . . There is also reason to believe that sound conservation work can be carried forward faster, and at a lower cost to all concerned when farmers decide to work together on it in groups in a really American neighborly way.

Generally, as you know, it is now the policy of many soil-conservation-district governing bodies to insist that district work be done through organized groups. Many districts have taken definite steps to further such group action, so that farmers with common problems and common interests will work together to the fullest possible extent. I believe this is a wise and rewarding policy on the part of the districts. . . .

Accordingly, I am asking all regional conservators, State conservationists, regional staffs, including zone conservationists, district conservationists, work-unit technicians, research specialists, and everyone else in the Service who is in a position to help, to take all appropriate steps possible in assisting soil-conservation districts with the development of group action in soil conservation.

Before 1948 regional and state SCS offices generally, except for Region IV, despite official SCS policy favoring the group approach, had not been exerting any considerable pressure on the districts. An examination of the work plans of the districts created in 1946-47 reveals that the districts expressing approval of group planning were scattered throughout the states at a ratio of about one to four. To insure that regional, state, and local SCS personnel actively got behind the drive for the group approach, the Chief of the Service concluded his 1948 letter by requiring a semi-annual report of each regional conservator: ". . . on the progress in his region of this highly important matter of helping farmers work together in compact, natural groups for soil conservation." According to the Chief of SCS, the Service's drive to get districts to work through neighbor groups was further intensified during 1950.

District supervisors have generally accepted the opinion of the Soil Conservation Service on the need for using the neighbor group approach to speed conservation. This is evidenced by the fact that, according to conservative estimates by the Service, more than one-half of the soil conservation districts are now working through neighbor groups. In 1950, the Service was working with nearly 18,000 neighbor groups, composed of more than 133,000 farmers. Within the next year, the number of neighbor groups working with districts had risen to 25,563. Over 190,000 farmers were working in these groups.[7]

The fact that supervisors have not taken an active part in priority determinations is also reflected in the pattern of priority decisions in districts before the Service led them to the group approach. Often, in such districts, supervisors either have not established any priority policies or have alluded to criteria for determining priorities in ill-defined and unsystematic terms. The order in which applications for assistance are received is probably the criterion set up most frequently for determining priorities. Yet this guide is to be used in connection with the criterion of geographical convenience. These guides are often further confused by an expression of the desirability of spotting conservation farms in all communities for their demonstrational value.

For example, the work plan of the Carlsbad District, New Mexico, declared that: ". . . one or more farms will be selected in each area upon which typical problems exist to serve as demonstration units." In the Orangeburg District, South Carolina, supervisors, according to the work plan, are to select: ". . . a few farms strategically located that would represent as many of the conservation practices as possible. These farms are to be used as model farms."

Another basis frequently used to supplement other criteria in establishing priorities is the relationship of each conservation job to the major conservation need or major conservation emphasis of the district. For example, the supervisors of the Van Buren District, Michigan, reported that the conservationist was instructed to assist farmers in approximately the same order as the applications were received with due regard for a higher priority where contour orchards were to be planted. In the Lynches River District, South Carolina, where drainage is considered the most important activity of the district, priority has been given to areas where drainage work is being done. A final criterion which is often added to the others is the interest of the farmers involved. For instance, the Gibson County District, Indiana, work plan declares that: "The priority of kind and location of work will be determined by the Board of Supervisors based upon the interest of the farmers involved."

Clearly in districts operating under such ambiguous combinations of priority policies, the real priority policies are being

---

[7] *Report of the Chief of the Soil Conservation Service,* 1950, p. 10; 1951, p. 9.

established in the day-to-day operations of the district. Thus, if supervisors are to determine priority policies they must meet frequently and be closely involved in district operations. They must, as the SCS state conservationist in Virginia put it, be on hand to say, "Well, you fellows seem to have worked long enough in A community, now shift over to B community." Otherwise, priority policies will in practice be made and carried out by the technicians in grouping their farm planning work for travel efficiency, or by the person who routes conservation equipment. Frequently, supervisors candidly admit, and district conservationists agree, that it is the technicians who are determining the order of work, that the supervisors give little priority guidance, with occasional exceptions when a supervisor indicates that he thinks a particular farmer should be expeditiously taken care of. On the other hand, the stronger boards who are making other policy decisions are making operating priority decisions.

Today perhaps half of the district governing bodies are giving at least formal routine approval to technicians' priority suggestions. A much smaller number is reserving the right to decide, as the Alpine District, Utah, supervisors put it: ". . . from month to month which area we will work in and which applications we will work with in the area." Until recently, however, supervisors in the majority of districts have not sufficiently felt the pressure of farmers wanting conservation assistance to appreciate the need for their making priority policy.

The fear is frequently expressed that the SCS responsibility for servicing ACP farmers and the new three-stage planning process will combine to deprive supervisors of much of their power to determine district policies. There is a real possibility, however, that the new procedures, together with widespread district adoption of the neighbor group approach in conservation, may stimulate greater supervisor participation in the important area of priority decisions.

The carrying on of conservation work through neighbor groups so reduces the number of major decisions required in setting up priorities for district assistance to farmers that supervisors are more likely to take a real part in making those decisions. For some time, SCS technicians and district boards each year have made "work load analyses" of the work for which district farmers have requested assistance, the time required for such work, and the man hours available. On the basis of this analysis, the district boards are to determine the order of assistance. Supervisors, it is reported, have been taking an increasingly active part in making these large decisions where blocs of farmers are affected.

Since SCS has become responsible for providing ACP farmers with technical assistance, priority decisions on the order of Service assistance to farmers becomes vital to district welfare. District supervisors have a new compelling reason for participation in the work load analysis which is now being made each spring to determine the amount of technical assistance ACP farmers and district cooperators will require during the season. In most counties, sufficient technical time is not yet available to do the total job requested. District boards, in these circumstances, have been strongly pressing district cooperators' prior claim to technician assistance.

With ACP farmers thronging into the district program, the groups of conservation farmers may soon become almost identical. Priority decisions will then largely turn on whether farmers in the initial or advanced stages of planning or farmers wishing to complete a farm plan should be given priority on technical time. This, in theory at least, is a decision which supervisors are to make. Already, however, regional variations in emphasis by technicians on one or another of the three stages are developing — an indication that this priority decision is now being made at the regional level of SCS rather than by local district boards.

Balancing the Phases of Conservation Activity

The balancing of conservation *education* with conservation *operations* and the balancing of farm planning with applying conservation treatments are two basic policy decisions in the scheduling of district activity. This is another policy area in which the contrasting background drives of the supervisors and the Service staff has given opportunity for blending divergent viewpoints into a proportioned approach to district activity.

CONSERVATION PLANNING AND APPLICATION OF PRACTICES

Convinced that adequate, permanent conservation cannot be achieved without the employment of the farm conservation plan, the Service has seen farm planning as the first step toward conservation. With an over-all view of the magnitude of the national conservation job in proportion to the personnel and resources available to carry on the work, the Service quite naturally emphasized first things first, that is, conservation planning. Moreover, SCS was sensitive to the need for compiling an impressive record of accomplishment, if it was to obtain from Congress adequate public funds for carrying on its work.

In its early years the SCS believed that the most effective way of "ringing the cash register" was by covering the districts as rapidly as possible with farm conservation plans. Thus, from the national level down through the region and the states, pressure has been put upon the farm planners in the districts to complete each year a maximum of farm plans. The technicians' accomplishment records have been judged very largely by the number of plans they turn off. In short, the Service in the past has had a tendency to push for farm planning at the expense of not carrying along, at a proportionate rate, assistance to farmers in the application of their plans.

Supervisors, in contrast, have been more sensitive to the need for getting conservation practices upon the land. The accumulation of proddings supervisors receive from their farmer acquaintances, waiting impatiently to receive promised technical assistance in putting their land under conservation treatment, makes them conscious that farmer interest in the program may be lost if application is allowed to lag too far behind planning.

The responsibility of determining whether Service technicians are to carry on planning or application is that of the district governing bodies. Yet, when SCS workers in a district are instructed, as Service employees, to complete a certain minimum of plans per year, the Service in effect is setting the ratio between planning and application. Throughout the country, however, there has been a definite tendency for governing bodies to push for the evening up of application and planning. The East Goodhue District, Minnesota, typifies supervisor awareness of the need for more application work. The supervisors state in an annual report:

It is the follow-up work that either spells success or failure with many of our conservation plans. We therefore ask that provisions and funds be provided so that more help can be made available to our district for this follow-up work on plans which have already been developed. Unless this is forthcoming our progress [in planning] must necessarily be slower from now on, or we shall miss our objective, namely establish soil conservation.

Another typical reaction is the terse request of the Central Valley District, New Mexico, for "fewer blueprints and more conservation."

The reaction against habitual SCS pressure for a rapidly

increasing number of farm plans was at one time especially noticeable in Region II, where there was a rigid quota of 80 farm
plans a year for each farm planner. The view of a commissioner
of the Northeast Mississippi District is representative of the
attitude of many supervisors in that region: "The way I've been
signing plans, I think they [the technicians] should cut their 80
plans — should concentrate on getting more of the things on the
ground."

Supervisors interviewed in Alabama and Tennessee were almost unanimous in stressing the impracticability of carrying
planning too far ahead of application. They could see no good
in ". . . working up plans just to have them on file." They voiced
their concern for giving farmers assistance in applying the plans
already developed. A supervisor of one Tennessee district saw
it as unfair that the farm planner in his county had been given
a ". . . little riding because he did not write his 80 plans last
year." He felt that the farm planner by working hard to get a
lot of conservation on the ground had been of greater aid to the
district than if he had written his quota of plans.

According to SCS officials, whenever a governing body sees
fit to direct that application work rather than planning be
largely emphasized in a district, the technicians are to follow the
supervisors' instructions. Quite frequently, the supervisors in
Region II have taken a stand for restoring a balance between
planning and application. For example, supervisors of one
Georgia district in an annual report insisted on the technicians
devoting their time to aiding in establishing practices upon the
farms already planned rather than greatly increasing the number
of plans:

> The temporary expedient which has been followed in the District
> during part of the year has resulted in a reduction of the number
> of farm plans developed. . . . We believe though, that this has been
> over-compensated for by the noticeable improvement in the applied
> program and a change to a more active [farmer] interest in doing
> something about the soil erosion and land management problem.
> More farm plans than can be properly serviced tend to lessen rather
> than accelerate interest.

Supervisors of another Georgia district also determined that
their technicians should concentrate their energies on applying
practices:

> . . . there was an increase in all phases of the establishment of
> practices on the land, although there was a decrease in the number

of plans written. . . . The supervisors consider the establishment of practices much more important at this stage of our program than the writing of additional plans.

Nevertheless, despite frequent examples of supervisors' acting to turn the technicians to application work, the establishment of farm planning quotas for Service technicians generally resulted in the Service's setting the balance. For in a majority of the districts, supervisors accepted without questioning the technician's obligation to prepare a minimum number of plans. As a supervisor in a Tennessee district explained: "We like to try to help our boys get enough applications to get their 80 plans." Even if supervisors felt a need for carrying on more application work in their district, they were often reluctant to override a Service policy.

If supervisors are to have their proper weight in striking the balance between planning and application, the method used in Region III for determining farm planning quotas for each technician is preferable. Here the district conservationists, after getting the views of the supervisors in their areas, work out with the state office what the quota of plans for each technician can suitably be. In this manner, the supervisors, being specifically consulted, are more likely to express their attitude toward a suitable ratio than if they have to speak out against a *fait accompli*.

The district conservationists, seeing the same local circumstances as farmer supervisors, often have the same realization of the value in keeping application abreast of planning. As a district conservationist in Wisconsin explained: "A paper plan is worthless until it is carried out. So why put all that time and effort into writing a plan unless it can be put to work upon the land itself before the farmer has lost interest in carrying it out." A district conservationist in a southern state believed so strongly that the Service's system of measuring its success by farm plans was faulty that he stated his views to the state conservationist in a letter which was forwarded to the regional office.

The Service has shown marked concern in recent years not only for accelerating the rate at which the farm lands of the districts actually come under conservation treatment, but for stepping up the rate of application in relation to planning. This concern has been in part the result of district governing bodies' belief in the need for balancing application with planning. The ratio of acres which have received combined conservation treatment to acres planned has moved steadily upward. The official figures of SCS indicate that in 1940, 45 per cent of the acres planned had received conservation treatment. In 1946, the ratio had moved to 50 per cent. In 1950, the ratio had risen to 56 per cent. By January, 1952, the ratio of acres treated to acres planned had climbed to 58.5 per cent.[8] Since these ratios are based on cumulative figures, the shift toward application in recent years is even greater than the percentages indicate.

During the calendar year 1951, 16.8 per cent of the total man hours of SCS professional and sub-professional personnel below the state level were being devoted to farm planning and 33.6 to application work.[9] Nevertheless, since it takes on an average 2.6 times as long to apply practices on an acre as to plan the same acre, application is still not keeping in time with planning. Comparing the ratio of application to planning does not adequately indicate, however, either the absolute increase in the number of acres receiving combined conservation treatment each year or the increased speed with which both the planning and application of practices is being carried on. Whereas in 1942, 5 million acres received conservation treatment, in 1950, 26 million acres were treated. This represented an increase of 388 per cent in acreage treated during a period when SCS facilities for carrying on conservation increased only 54 per cent.[10]

The adoption of the new three-stage planning process represents a culmination in the Service's gradual shift in emphasis from planning to application. Under the three step procedure, there is a real danger that farmers will never take the third step of developing a rounded farm conservation plan. Rather, they may be content to carry out those individual practices which pay off in quick economic returns. Even when a farmer was required to accept a complete farm plan before he could receive district assistance, farmers often would only adopt those practices which would rapidly increase their income, and would fail to carry out those parts of their plans which called for shifts from cropland to permanent grass and legumes.

SCS officials are aware of the danger to a rounded conservation program inherent in the three stage process, and they are still convinced that a rounded program on each farm is finally neces-

---

[8] "Analysis of Soil Conservation Service Work," *op. cit.*, p. 4.
[9] *Ibid*, p. 11.
[10] U. S. Congress. House Committee on Appropriations. *Hearings before the Subcommittee on the Agriculture Department Appropriation Bill for 1952.* 82nd Cong., 1st Sess., pp. 783, 784.
[11] *Ibid.*, p. 784.

sary if the nation's soil is to be conserved. Undoubtedly the Service will still act as a force for the development of a balanced and complete conservation plan for each individual farm. In setting up the new method for reporting technician accomplishments, for example, provision is being made for showing the movement of district farmers from year to year into the advanced and final stages of conservation planning.

CONSERVATION EDUCATION WITH OPERATIONS

Supervisors, in their reluctance to permit planning to spur too far ahead of application, have probably aided in bringing about an adjustment in conservation activity which has put conservation administration upon a sounder footing. The common supervisor inclination for balancing operations with education follows a similar attitude pattern. This supervisor preference, however, would probably eventuate in the slowing down of all conservation activity if it were to dominate in conservation administration.

It is a quite prevalent supervisor view that since the district is receiving far more applications for assistance than it can service, it is unnecessary — even unwise — to carry on further educational or promotional work in the district. This belief rests upon the solid fact that there is a nation-wide backlog of 200,000 formal requests for farm plans which cannot be attended to in the near future.[11] It is an opinion which largely grows out of supervisor awareness of the impatience with which farmers await planning works being carried out by the district. An annual report of the Calhoun County District, Mississippi, describes this farmer attitude:

> There is quite a bit of disappointment expressed over the slowness of planning work. When communities turn in applications for conservation work, they expect technicians to start planning work the next day. They are very anxious for conservation maps of their farms, and it seems impossible to explain why they have to wait a month or longer for this mapping to be done.

In consequence, district boards have wanted the educational work held in check. As an instance, the governing body of the Kittitas District, Washington, purposely left the educational work of the district undeveloped because too many applications were already on hand. The Sanpete County District, Utah, felt it inadvisable to distribute educational literature on conservation or seek newspaper publicity because of its large backlog of applications. Again, the supervisors of Winooski District, Vermont, have held it impractical to work for further applications. The Board of the Greenbrier Valley District, West Virginia, felt that since farmers were having to wait so long for technical help in planning their farms, it was undesirable to carry on further educational meetings. There is abundant evidence of this supervisor reaction against further educational work when a backlog of applications is on hand.

In contrast, professional agriculture workers usually realize:

". . . that the interest developed in the educational and other pre-district meetings may be confined to a relatively small per cent of the total farmers or ranchers living within that area. That, without continued educational work to develop interest among the other percentage sooner or later we may reach a stalemate in the program of conservation within the district." [12]

It is the district governing bodies' job to determine how, where, and when the assistance they have accepted from agencies for carrying on the district's educational program is to be used. Yet, it is questionable if the decision to carry on conservation education in an area should be a strictly local one. Making the rural population conservation conscious may be so important a national concern that the decision to educate or not to educate in conservation cannot be left to the whims of local people or to the exigencies of local affairs. Here, then, the wider viewpoint of agency representatives should be a guiding influence in making district decisions upon educational work.

Developing Equipment Programs

Providing district cooperators with the equipment necessary for applying conservation plans involves another series of policy decisions. Although the Soil Conservation Service has felt that it had a special public responsibility for seeing that the machinery it makes available to districts is suitably used, there is a wide area of equipment policy completely left to the supervisors. Many of the equipment decisions the district must make are outside the jurisdiction of the Service. For SCS has been able to supply only a minor percentage of the equipment needed in conservation activity. Since farmers are familiar with machinery, supervisors have not been reluctant to express their views on machinery policies.

---

[12] N. E. Beers, Assistant Director, Montana Extension Service, "Extension's Contribution to Soil Conservation District Programs," address before Fifth Annual Meeting of the Montana Association of Soil Conservation District Supervisors, Billings, Montana, December 18, 19, 1946. Minutes.

POLICIES IN EQUIPMENT PROCUREMENT

Farmer supervisor thinking upon the various methods for procuring equipment necessarily varies from district to district. Discussions in area meetings of district supervisors in Utah brought out that, even within a single state, districts cannot adopt the same equipment policies:

It was evident that every district had its own local problems and that no two districts could or would operate alike due to a number of factors such as availability of contractor equipment, availability of efficient tractor drivers, amount of equipment on hand when district was formed and the types of jobs and practices to be carried out.[13]

Nevertheless, despite varying local circumstances, certain common supervisor attitude patterns concerning equipment can be distinguished. As the former Chief of the Service has pointed out, there has always been a demand from districts for much more equipment than the Service could supply. Yet, peculiarly enough, there is a nation-wide supervisor preference for using contract machinery when it is suitably available within a district. Surprisingly, also, there is some tendency for governing bodies to prefer purchasing their own equipment to using SCS equipment. A preponderance of districts, of course, always express a need for more SCS equipment in their annual reports. The large number of districts which do not voice any desire for more Service machinery is the significant fact.

The attitudes of the district governing bodies in New Mexico toward securing equipment are perhaps typical of supervisor opinions in other states. "Over one-half of the districts," the New Mexico State Committee, in summarizing one year's district reports, declares, "made quite an issue of the need for more equipment." A significant number of the districts wanting more machinery, however, were not looking to the Service to supply it. Only a few New Mexico districts seemed to be greatly disappointed in not being able to secure more heavy equipment from the Soil Conservation Service. At least two districts in the State (Grant and Sierra) refused a loan of heavy equipment from the Soil Conservation Service. On the other hand, a good number of New Mexico districts were exploring ways and means of obtaining finances so that they could purchase their own equipment. For example, the Otero and Mora-San Miguel Dis-

---

[13] "Report on Five Area Meetings held for Soil Conservation District Supervisors," week of February 17, 1947, at Ogden, Provo, Cedar City, Richfield, and Price, Utah, prepared by Utah State Soil Conservation Committee.

tricts wanted FSA credit regulations changed in order that they might borrow money for purchasing equipment.

This supervisor attitude pattern toward equipment is reflected in all sections of the country. The most common supervisor answers to the writer's question concerning the need for more machinery were "Oh, we could use more . . . we don't want to fool with any more machinery . . . machinery only gives us a lot of headaches." Overseeing the operation and maintenance of machinery as well as collecting and accurately accounting for rentals upon it is generally viewed as a bother. Two districts in Montana now completely relying on contractors explained their satisfaction thus:[14]

Wibaux District:

This eliminated a great deal of record keeping, maintenance problems and, most important of all, financial losses to our district. Board members and work unit personnel were all pleased with the way it worked out.

Little Beaver District:

We consider one of the improvements made the past season is having all the dirt work done by contract instead of by government-loaned equipment. In 1945 we moved about a total of 62,000 cubic yards of dirt, and using government-loaned equipment, the district lost about $500 on the season's operation. This year, by using contract labor the district cleared about $1300 on the dirt work. It is planned to use contract labor again the coming season if possible, as it relieves the supervisors as well as the SCS technicians of a lot of time and responsibility, thus allowing more time to be spent for the application of conservation to the land.

Particularly have supervisors thought it unfeasible to handle small equipment such as grain drills, harrows, and plows. Yet, one Utah district board adopted a policy of referring all heavy equipment work to contractors, but of owning small equipment and having it on hand for cooperators at a cost sufficient to take care of operation, maintenance, and replacements.[15]

In many districts, before contract equipment was becoming so generally available, supervisors' disinterest in equipment was symptomatic of their weakness as a governing body, their lack of any real interest in having an action program which would get conservation onto the land. Now, however, with increasing

---

[14] Minutes, Montana Supervisors Annual Meeting, *op. cit.*

[15] "Report of Five Area Meetings," *op. cit.* In expending its fiscal 1947 equipment appropriation of $2,500,000, SCS endeavored so far as possible to purchase large equipment.

numbers of contractors going in for conservation work, districts interested in an aggressive program of operation can nevertheless "get out of the equipment business."

SCS-Loaned Equipment

As in some of the New Mexico districts, supervisor disinterest in equipment has in frequent cases been limited to a disinclination for "fooling with government equipment." As one comissioner in a Mississippi district put it in an annual report: "We got enough machines [draglines]. . . . Had a new one move into my county last month. We don't need to fool around with a Government machine." A supervisor in a Tennessee district explained his reluctance to being held responsible for a government machine. He saw himself as a potential target for charges from "local folks" of "playing politics."

The few reported cases of district non-acceptance of SCS equipment reflect a rather general supervisor impatience, as lay citizens, with government red tape in accounting for the use and maintenance of equipment. For example, all except six New Mexico districts expressed a need for help in keeping district equipment accounts. One district believed that SCS should keep the books.

The very fact that the Service, first due to war shortages and then to lack of equipment appropriations, has been unable to provide the districts with little machinery except that left over from demonstration and CCC camp work, has also been partly responsible for any supervisor disinterest in SCS equipment. Not only have district governing bodies somewhat disengaged their minds from securing equipment from this source, as prospects of obtaining it diminished, but the trouble and cost of keeping old machinery in repair has been a sour note. For instance, about a third of the New Mexico districts expressed themselves as being greatly disappointed in the Soil Conservation Service's not being able to furnish more assistance in keeping in repair heavy equipment. The equipment committee of the Montana supervisors' association recommended that obsolete earth moving equipment be sold to the highest bidder rather than put on loan to districts. State and district conservationists and farmer supervisors from a cross section of the country have repeatedly pointed out supervisor dissatisfaction in being unable to build up reserve funds sufficient for new equipment because of the excessive cost of repairing the old.

Usually, however, supervisor dissatisfaction with Service loaned equipment has not been strong enough to lead districts to refuse such equipment. The chief of the Administrative Services Division, SCS, has stated that although districts have sometimes refused the loan of equipment, such district action is not at all typical.

In summary, then, although the districts have seen the Soil Conservation Service as the likeliest source of the equipment so essential to carrying on conservation, they generally prefer using contract equipment or an outright gift of equipment for which it is unnecessary to make any accounting. As an SCS official put it: "What the average board of supervisors would like would be for SCS to get the equipment, and grant it to the supervisors. It's only natural for supervisors to want to have complete control over equipment."

This supervisor attitude coincides with the official policy which Service officials have always emphasized — that SCS can only supply a small portion of the equipment needed. The Service has a long established rule of not putting any machinery into a district where such machinery is already available. It was the first to push for the district use of private contractors for carrying out conservation work. The official in charge of the SCS equipment program was reflecting general Service opinion when he explained that "from the long-range standpoint, the contractor method is best, since equipment is neither the Service's nor the districts' primary business."

In recent years, there has been a noticeable trend toward the Service's getting completely out of the equipment field. By the end of the fiscal year 1951, SCS had only 275 pieces of major equipment on loan to districts, as compared to 700 pieces in 1950, 1,011 in 1949, 1,144 in 1948, and correspondingly larger amounts for the preceding years. These 275 pieces of primary equipment represent less than one per cent of the total now being used in the districts.[16]

A composite of factors has brought on this trend. Although SCS officials do not publicly proclaim it, the administration of the equipment program has been costly in terms of both SCS man hours and equipment losses, nor has it always repaid sufficiently in terms of stimulating local activity in conservation. Not only have SCS field employees had to take valuable time

---

[16] *See* annual Soil Conservation Service tables on "Private Contractors and Soil Conservation District Equipment."

from operations field work to perform such regularly assigned duties as equipment inspection, but they have largely carried the supervisors' work in the equipment field also. Quite commonly they have routed the machinery, employed and directed machine operators, and have overseen machinery repair. Although governing bodies have felt the accounts and reports they must make upon SCS loaned equipment to be largely unnecessary and irksome, the Service has not always been able to secure suitable use and disposition of equipment.

The Service is increasingly realizing that using the availability of SCS machinery as a stimulus for organizing a district has not paid off in actual conservation returns in districts which have been organized almost solely upon the basis of the machinery incentive. In the first place, districts which have been organized upon the anticipation of SCS machinery are often disappointed and disgruntled by the amount of machinery SCS is able to make available to them. District anual reports raise this point more often perhaps than any other problem. Secondly, as one state conservationist pointed out, when districts are organized because local people are only interested in getting a piece of machinery, such as a dragline, to do one particular kind of conservation job, state and federal professional agricultural workers later are often unable to stir up farmer interest in a general soil conserving program. For these reasons the Service has been steadily granting outright to the district a major portion of the equipment it has for distribution.

The special circumstances of World War II shortages and economy-minded Congresses have combined with this SCS policy to put the Service practically out of the equipment distribution field. The Service's experience in attempting to spend its 1947 equipment appropriation, during a period of inflated prices and inferior materials, probably resulted in an inclination among SCS officials not to press Congress very hard for further equipment appropriations. Thus, no concerted push has been made by SCS for an equipment appropriation in recent years. The last equipment appropriation was for fiscal 1947.

Of course, if the inclination of certain congressmen to deluge the districts with a flood of Service purchased equipment should prevail, the Service would accept such equipment responsibilities with alacrity. For the SCS realizes that when it has only its technical services to offer the districts, its ability to persuade the districts to establish and operate effective conservation programs will be appreciably lessened. But, the Washington office believes that it is not in the cards for SCS to be given money for the purchase of new equipment.

Contract Equipment

Whatever the combination of causes may be, the Soil Conservation Service today is not nearly meeting the machinery needs of the ever-growing number of conservation districts. District governing bodies must therefore make their own independent determinations as to how to provide a large part of the equipment necessary for carrying out the conservation work of the district. Supervisor boards most commonly, as already observed, prefer to use contract equipment.

As the permanence of the district has become accepted, as districts have spread out over more and more rural areas, and as increasing numbers of farmers within each district carry on conservation work, the number of equipment contractors seeking to specialize in district work has multiplied. At the end of the 1951 fiscal year, 18,542 private contractors, using 50,086 major pieces of equipment, were working with soil conservation districts. This represented 96 per cent of all the heavy equipment used in districts throughout the United States. The number of private conservation contractors has increased rapidly since 1945. Since 1948, they have increased at a rate of about 1,600 a year.[17]

The increased availability of private equipment through contract has, in its turn, stimulated the districts to utilize contract equipment. Recently organized districts quite frequently have declared it their policy to use contract equipment as much as possible. For example, the district work plan of the Missoula County District, Montana, explains:

> Since there are a large number of earth moving contractors working in this vicinity, it will be the policy of the District to make use of their services. It is believed that by following this procedure, rather than by owning our own machinery, it will cost our cooperators no more for the work done and will relieve the technicians to work full time on the technical part of the conservation jobs.

So strong has been the swing of supervisor sentiment toward the use of contract equipment that at the national meeting of district supervisors in late 1950 there was considerable supervisor sentiment for actually selling district owned equipment to con-

---

[17] *Ibid.*

Fig. 8 — Terraces built on Iowa land and seeded to brome-clover-crested wheat mixture. The average slope for the 18 miles of terrace is 25 per cent.

Fig. 9 — Some of the decisions involved in developing a basic conservation farm plan.

tractors and for the handling of all of the earth moving jobs on a contract basis.[18]

A governing body's decision to contract with private equipment owners is entirely outside the jurisdiction of the Service. Nevertheless, the experience which SCS personnel has accumulated in watching districts throughout the country working with contractors should be given to districts as a basis for formulating their equipment policies. The assistant state conservationist, in Minnesota, emphasized that before a district decides to depend in a major degree upon contract equipment, the following considerations should be brought to its attention: Are the kinds of equipment required to meet the particular conservation jobs of the area privately available? Will there be a sufficient quantity of equipment to carry out the work of the district? Is district ownership of equipment also necessary to lower and stabilize the price of work to cooperators? How dependable will the particular contractors available for district work be in carrying out their work?

Although the Service has a policy of not recommending rental rates for government owned machinery which substantially undercut private contractors, the rates for contract equipment are generally somewhat higher than those for district equipment. SCS experience has indicated that it is sometimes necessary to have Service- or district-owned equipment in a district to keep commercial rates in line. For example, when districts in North Dakota started draining lands in the Red River Valley, commercial contractors undertook to set their rates to farmers at a figure twice as high as necessary. But when the Service began pouring its equipment into the area, contract rates came into line. The Montana Supervisors Association's equipment committee believed it advisable for the districts to stay in competition with the commercial contractors. It recommended that each district own at least part of its equipment.

The problem which the Service has found the districts most commonly encountering in using contractors has been a lack of contractor dependability and the difficulty in getting contractors to live up to a high standard of workmanship. A part of the solution to this problem lies in the districts' adopting adequate policies for dealing with contractors.

---

[18] U. S. Congress. House Committee on Appropriations. *Hearing before the Subcommittee on the Agriculture Department Appropriation Bill for 1952.* 82nd Cong., 1st Sess., p. 794.

Service personnel have learned that, for a district to use contract equipment effectively, the proper respective functions and obligations of the district and the contractor must be determined. They must be specifically set forth and agreed to by both parties in a binding fashion. That is, suitable contracts must be used. The district, it is generally agreed, should take the responsibility for lining up the work, routing equipment, and making all charges and collections. In return for a contractor's obligating himself to do district work exclusively, the district may well guarantee a certain amount of work and payment for the work. Most important, the contractor must agree to perform the work in accordance with specifications of the Service technicians. It should be agreed that district payment to the contractor will be withheld if the technician so recommends.

Supervisor discussions in their annual state meetings reveal that district boards are becoming increasingly aware of the need for nailing down desirable responsibilities and obligations in contractor-district contracts. As alert district supervisors gain experience in using contract equipment for district work, they usually recognize the need for contracts. The experience related by a supervisor in a Tennessee district illustrates how supervisors learn, through experience, the need for contracts:

We made a mistake in not having a written contract with the fellow who purchased a tractor on priority after the war to do district work. After he got his tractor, he soon found more profitable business for his machine, and has about quit doing district work.

Most frequently the district acts merely as a catalytic agent in bringing the farmer and contractor together. But districts are steadily moving toward the use of district contracts with commercial contractors.

District-Purchased Equipment

Because of the increasing amount of satisfactory contract equipment available to districts, a district which does not choose to operate its own equipment is not confining itself to relative inaction. Yet, contract equipment and SCS equipment have, in terms of conservation accomplishment, been profitably supplemented by equipment obtained through other means. Many of the vigorous districts, particularly in the Great Plains and Southern Great Plains, are choosing to build up their own equipment capital.[19]

[19] SCS estimates that districts in Regions V and VI have probably gone farthest in purchasing their own equipment, but that districts in Regions II, IV, and VII are close behind in district-purchased equipment.

The districts, in 1951, owned an estimated $9,000,000 worth of equipment and machinery.[20] Although district ownership of equipment has been increasing significantly, the increase has been relatively slow in comparison to the rapidity with which contractor equipment has multiplied. Thus, although the districts have increased their ownership of major pieces of conservation equipment from 777 in 1948 to 1,486 in 1951, district owned and operated equipment represents only about three per cent of the total pieces of equipment in use in the districts.[21]

The districts have adopted a variety of policies for raising money for the purchase of equipment. The various methods which have been used by Nebraska supervisors are representative of the means used in a cross section of districts. The most usual method has been to include a replacement charge in setting the rates on SCS loaned or granted equipment. A number of districts have used the contract system as a means of raising district funds. A supervisor from Burt County District reported his group's making "a charge of fifty cents an hour for the district, for lining up the work so that we can get some equipment for ourselves."[22] Another Nebraska district has leased 100,000 acres of marginal land from the federal government and then leases it out to cooperators in the district. "We lease it out at a little greater expense than what we take it in for," explained a supervisor from that district.[23]

Other districts have furnished seeds and other supplies to district cooperators at a slight profit. Another common way of raising money for purchasing equipment has been for supervisors to borrow through their local bank. Signing a note, they make themselves personally liable for the down payment of perhaps 20–30 per cent of the cost of the equipment, and the bank takes a mortgage on the equipment for the rest. As a supervisor from the Gage County District explained this procedure: "Mr. Allington (a fellow supervisor) and I put our names on the note and the banker said, 'Go ahead'."[24] He continued:

I don't think we should make this appear too discouraging. It might so appear that the supervisors would lose something, but we get a lot out of it so there will be just a small chance. I think it is of public interest. You can deduct it from your income taxes. I believe that it isn't such a bad thing for the Board of Supervisors to buy this

[20] House Appropriation *Hearings,* 1952, *op. cit.,* p. 794.
[21] *See* SCS annual tables on "Private Contractors and SCD Equipment," *op. cit.*
[22] Proceedings, Nebraska Supervisors Association, *op. cit.,* p. 13.
[23] *Ibid.,* p. 22.
[24] *Ibid.,* p. 10.

equipment. It would be about 100 to 1 that you might lose on it. The risk isn't so great.

Supervisors in some cases have gone to the length of personally lending money to their districts. The West Virginia Extension soil conservationist states that, in his state, district funds have been earned by the supervisors being interested enough in the program to be willing in many cases personally to lend money to the districts. In the Portneuf District, Idaho, district-landowner contracts for land leveling were drawn up as negotiable instruments, which served to secure money from a local bank for the purchase of tractors and carryalls. District rental charges on the equipment were used to retire the notes held by the bank.

Other districts have successfully raised funds for equipment through private subscriptions. As an instance, in the Harrison County District, Missouri, local supporters financed the purchasing of two heavy outfits for constructing earth dams for ponds, drainage work, and terracing.

State and County Equipment

Districts also have commonly sought the loan of equipment from state and county agencies. For example, the Wyoming District, New York, has rented machinery from the state highway department. In West Virginia, several boards of supervisors have recently reported that they had made very satisfactory arrangements with the local representatives of the State Road Commission for lending equipment.

Although the county government repeatedly has been pointed to as a rich source of equipment for districts, supervisors frequently have seen the inadvisability of attempting to borrow county highway equipment for conservation use. One of the advantages often cited for the "Wisconsin system" is that it facilitates the use of county equipment by the districts. In Wisconsin, the agricultural committee of the county board of supervisors serves ex officio as the soil conservation district supervisors. The agricultural committee is made up of the chairman of the county board of supervisors, three farmers appointed by the county board (one being a member) and the county superintendent of schools. Yet supervisors in Wisconsin, being also members of their county boards, often have pointed out the impracticability of using county equipment. As a Wisconsin supervisor explained: "The county usually needs its machinery for working the roads at those times of year when conservation work should be done. It doesn't look fair to see county machinery, which belongs to everyone, being used on the land of one farmer when the county roads need fixing." A Nebraska supervisor from the Nuckolls County District, who was also a county commissioner, voiced the same view:

> In regard to getting work done in cooperation with the county, I think that most of the county boards are very willing to go out there but from the taxpayers' standpoint, I doubt if the plan is advisable. Regardless of what you may charge a farmer for working on his farm, if the taxpayer over the hill is left with a bad road, he has a right to complain. I don't think the County Board should hire out the equipment if it is needed on the roads. I don't know of any time in the last three years when county equipment could go out — when it wasn't needed somewhere. The district should arrange to own its own machinery.[25]

Again this viewpoint was expressed by a Florida supervisor from the Holmes Creek District:

> Our district covers part of two counties and the Holmes Creek District has more equipment than both counties put together, so I don't believe our county commissioners would be in a position to help us.[26]

Thus, boards of supervisors often have not seen fit to push for the use of county highway equipment. Supervisors, however, generally have supported the efforts of their state associations to secure state appropriations for the purchase of equipment for the districts.

Governing bodies necessarily have made their own policy decision about procuring equipment in addition to that made available by the Service. Technicians might advise and guide them in developing their equipment policies, but the supervisors alone could make the decision. Their very failure to make a decision is indeed the negative one of limiting the activity of the district.

Supervisors generally have shown considerable capacity to make technical and practical decisions on the utility of various types of machinery for doing specific conservation jobs. This technical competence of supervisors in appraising machinery is reflected again and again in the spontaneous discussions of supervisors at their state association meetings.

[25] Proceedings, Nebraska Supervisors Association, *op. cit.*, p. 16.
[26] Minutes, Annual Meeting of the Florida Association of Soil Conservation District Supervisors, Gainesville, Florida, September 25, 26, 1946, p. 14.

EQUIPMENT OPERATING POLICIES

In the area of equipment operating policies, Service technicians generally have accepted the lead in pointing up the decision which should be taken by supervisors. The Service staff, of course, has a special responsibility toward Service loaned equipment. Official SCS policy declares:

> It is expected, therefore, that the SCS technicians in the District will assist the supervisors in making the most efficient utilization of all loaned equipment. This assistance may include selection and training of operators, advice on routing of the equipment, recommendations regarding repair and maintenance, and guidance in the preparation of cost estimates.[27]

The Service recognizes that: "The Soil Conservation District Supervisors will, in most cases, be unable to devote a large portion of their time to the management of the equipment and also that many of these men have had very little experience in handling such equipment."[28]

Supervisors, in their daily intimate knowledge of machinery, have gained competency in dealing with machinery problems. Yet they generally are prone to accept without hesitation all equipment operating policies suggested by the technicians, with the single exception of rates to be charged farmer-cooperators for the use of machinery. As a public agency receiving its machinery through public funds, the Service feels that it has a responsibility for establishing machinery rental rates to farmers sufficient for the continued operation of government equipment, that is, sufficient for repair and amortization.

Therefore, the Service requires that the district's rates to farmers be sufficient to enable the district to pay into an equipment repair account at a rate adequate to cover the cost of repairing loaned machinery. Perceiving that there is small likelihood of future national equipment appropriations of any size, SCS feels that rates on SCS machinery should also be high enough to permit the districts to build up funds for the purchase of their own equipment. The Service states that one of the five objectives for which SCS equipment is to be loaned a district is: " . . . to assist the district, as determined by the district governing body, in building a sinking fund for the purchase of conservation equipment."[29] Finally, the Service realizes that

---

[27] "District Cooperation" SCS Field Memorandum No. 16, January 16, 1940, pp. 3, 4.
[28] *Ibid.*, p. 3.
[29] "Equipment for Loan to Districts," *op. cit.*, p. 1.

if district equipment rates are set too low, one source of equipment available to farmer-cooperators may be dried up. Private contractors may not find it economically feasible to compete with district equipment.

For these reasons, the Service sets up minimum rates, which districts are to accept in their equipment usage plans.

These rates have been found to be about the minimum needed for adequate repair and replacement costs of new or completely rebuilt equipment. They are not considered adequate to cover any costs beyond repair and replacement. While the Service may approve plans meeting these base rates, it strongly recommends that districts give full consideration to the condition of each piece of equipment available for loan to it and to the type of work on which it will be used, before establishing their rental rate schedules.[30]

In contrast, the supervisor attitude toward the rental rates to be charged farmers for machinery has been quite commonly marked by the psychology of government subsidy. They have the feeling that farmers should not be charged, or at least only nominally, for the use of a government machine. This attitude is also a part of the pattern of supervisor reaction against the district's bearing the cost of upkeep and repair of SCS machinery. According to state and district conservationists, district supervisors have generally reacted against what they consider the steepness of the minimum rates set up by the Service.

Although cases of district protest of SCS rate schedules are not usual, they have been frequent enough to indicate a quite general supervisor feeling against them. So strongly did the supervisors of the Ness County District, Kansas, object to the new set of rates fixed by the Service, in 1946, that they offered argument in their annual report:

We district supervisors feel that the setting aside of $1.50 per hour from the funds collected for the use of the D-4 tractor and scraper as required by Memorandum SCS 324-E is very unfair to the Ness County District. To begin with, the District, not the government, owns the scraper, and $1.50 per hour is excessive for the Caterpillar rate for repair and maintenance of the tractor. The D-4 tractor was in a poor condition when it arrived in Ness County. We have made all necessary minor repairs, had one complete overhaul job done on it, and still we have probably not averaged over 30c per hour for repair and maintenance. The State Mechanic rated it as being in good condition when he inspected it just recently. During the past year the tractor was operated a total of 1274 hours, which, had these regulations concerning

---

[30] "Equipment Operation Plan," *op. cit.*, p. cont'd.

the Repair and Maintenance Fund been in effect then, would have required us to lay aside $1,911 for repairs. This would be approximately one third of the cost of a new tractor and on this basis we feel that we would be making a sounder economic investment to purchase a new tractor of our own.

In one year in South Dakota, six district boards refused to sign the revised equipment usage plans because the schedule of rates seemed out of line.

Although the Service usually tries to insist that SCS rates be accepted as minimums, districts have sometimes set their own rates. "In cases of protest," the SCS official in charge of administrative services declared, "the regional offices will lean over backwards to adjust them if at all reasonable." In the case of the protesting South Dakota districts, for example, the regional office felt it expedient to revise the rates downward to the supervisors' satisfaction.

Despite the Service's belief in the necessity for persuading districts to charge at least the minimum rate, SCS personnel have sometimes failed during the organizational period of the district adequately to explain the obligations and limitations placed upon districts receiving SCS machinery. The fact that districts attempting to operate on their own rates generally have discovered that they are going into the red, and consequently later accepted SCS rate determinations, proves to the Service the soundness of its view.

PERFORMANCE OF DISTRICT MANAGEMENT ACTIVITIES

In addition to their policy forming functions, supervisors, in the governing of their district are to perform a series of concrete administrative activities: preparation of documents embodying their broad, formal substantive and procedural policies; reviewing and criticizing farm plans; routing equipment and overseeing its maintenance and repair; procuring and distributing materials; collecting, handling and using district funds; keeping accounts, preparing correspondence and reports; hiring and supervising any such district employees as district managers, machinery operators, and district conservation aids; and negotiating contracts.

Meeting of District Board

It is in the pattern of supervisor performance of their primary activity — meeting together as the governing body of the district

— that the extent to which supervisors carry on their policy forming functions and executive activities can be gauged. The frequency, regularity, and attendance of supervisor meetings, and the degree to which supervisors control such meetings, bear directly upon the exercising of policy forming functions by governing bodies.

FREQUENCY AND REGULARITY OF SESSIONS

Frequency of supervisor meetings ranges from a single meeting a year to weekly meetings. A small minority of districts holds only one or two meetings a year. In contrast, another very small minority of districts, such as the McIntosh County District, Oklahoma, meets weekly. A slightly larger number, such as the Kittitas District, Washington, have reported that they meet every two weeks. The general trend, however, has been for districts to turn to quarterly or monthly meetings.

In Tennessee, districts are encouraged to meet on a quarterly basis, although several districts such as the Robertson, Haywood, and Gibson County Districts have been meeting on a monthly basis. The trend toward monthly board meetings is even more pronounced. In California, district governing bodies are required by state law to meet once a month. In North Dakota, it is reported that, with few exceptions, regular monthly meetings are scheduled and attended by all supervisors. The majority of boards in Florida are reported to be holding regular monthly meetings. In all states, at least two or three districts record in their annual reports the holding of monthly meetings. These reports reveal that at least a quarter of the districts are now meeting monthly.

There also has been a trend in the districts toward the establishment of regularly scheduled meetings — such as the first Saturday in the month, every other Thursday evening, every second Friday, one meeting every three months, and so on. The observation of the Kansas state conservationist is quite typical of a trend in a majority of states: "Practically all Boards of Supervisors have established regular meeting dates and time of meeting, rather than merely meeting upon call."

Frequency, regularity, attendance, and supervisor leadership of meetings often intermesh to form patterns of strong or weak supervisor administrations. An examination of district annual reports reveals that governing bodies in the districts where regular meeting dates are set, meet much more frequently than boards in districts where meetings are called either by the chairman or a professional agricultural worker.

In addition, the amount of district business requiring the attention of the supervisors increases almost proportionately with the number of meetings held. Governing bodies meeting only once or twice a year are not making, and cannot make, district policy decisions. The reason given by a supervisor in a midwestern state for holding only two meetings was that the supervisors had no business to consider. And, indeed, there could be little business to consider. For decisions do not wait over long periods. Policy decisions in such districts are likely being made on a daily basis by the technicians.

In contrast, a board which meets monthly has a wealth of problems to consider. For example, the Carroll County District, Illinois, which meets the second Thursday of every month recently reported the following agenda:

January 9—Annual report – work plan for next year
February 13—Review plans – review of duties of directors
March 13—Plans for spring work and demonstrations
April 10—Plans for spring work – neighborhood locations
May 8—Open
June 12—Plans for tours and summer work
July 10—Review conservation needs
August 14—Review of conservation needs
September 11—Location of groups for planning
October 9—Check farm plans and procedure
November 13—Open
December 11—Annual Report – plans for next year

SUPERVISOR ATTENDANCE

The fact that frequent, regular meetings result in supervisors having a real job to do is reflected in an increase in supervisor interest in attending meetings. There is a real correlation between the regularity of meetings and high attendance of meetings. Boards which do not hold regularly scheduled meetings often report that attendance of members also has been irregular. Numerous districts which have no regular meeting dates report that their supervisors' meetings often have lacked a quorum. For example, in one midwestern district which has been holding only about two meetings a year, the district conservationist reports that only two of the five supervisors could be coaxed into coming to the annual meeting of the board.

In contrast, districts holding regular, frequent meetings record high supervisor attendance in their annual reports. For example, the supervisors of the Shiloh-O'Fallon District, Illinois, report that they have held monthly meetings since the District was organized and only on rare occasions has a member been absent. Attendance of the bi-weekly supervisor meetings in the Kittitas District, Washington, has averaged about 80 per cent. In North Dakota, where district boards with few exceptions are meeting monthly, attendance is reported as very high. In Florida, also, almost full attendance is reported at the monthly meetings of a majority of the districts.

SUPERVISOR LEADERSHIP IN MEETINGS

Frequent, regularly scheduled meetings have also generally coincided with the meetings in which supervisors play an active part. Not only are supervisors who meet infrequently ill-equipped in background knowledge necessary for making decisions, but the lead in organizing the meeting is generally taken by the professional agricultural worker. Almost invariably in the districts where the governing body meets only on call, the district conservationist or farm planner makes the determination to hold a supervisor meeting. Thus it is a government agency employee, rather than the supervisors, who is selecting the policy questions upon which the governing body is to act. The following are typical explanations of the reasons for holding board meetings in districts where supervisors meet only on call. For one district in the West it is reported that supervisors are called together " . . . only when the SCS personnel has something that needs to be decided by the supervisors." In another district in the South, supervisor meetings are " . . . most often the results of conferences of Soil Conservation Service and Extension workers where they determine that the board should be called to act on certain matters pertaining to district operation."

It is most commonly in the districts where supervisors meet on call that the district conservationist or sometimes the county agent is reported preparing the agenda without consulting with the supervisors. For instance, in the above mentioned western district, supervisors "take up the work which has been outlined by the SCS technicians." Supervisors, out of touch with the district program because of infrequent meetings and coming together to consider only the problems raised by the professional workers, almost invariably accept the views of the technicians as to how such problems should be met.

In contrast, boards meeting frequently and consequently

having an opportunity to keep in close touch with the problems of the districts and the work of the technicians often see problems to consider and questions to raise with the technicians in board meetings. As a result, these boards can take real part in developing agendas for their meetings and in making policy determinations. This general pattern of weak and strong supervisor administrations has been commonly observed by state and district conservationists in widely scattered sections of the country.

Preparation of District Program and Work Plan

If the role of governing bodies in determing district policies were to be measured by the part they have played in the original formal drafting of the district's policies, it could be safely concluded that the supervisors have had only a minor voice in making the policies of the districts. District governing bodies generally have followed, with little questioning, the lead of the Service in this first concrete task of a district's administration. Not only are the new supervisors uncertain as to how to go about organizing for community conservation action, but they commonly can see little real significance in preparing a formal program.

From the viewpoint of the Service, supervisors have been too content to leave this job to the Service staff. A perusal of district programs and work plans is sufficient to show that a preponderance of them are largely the work of professional agricultural workers. Not only do the work plans of districts within a state often have a similarity which cannot be wholly coincidental; but their tone and language is typically that of the professional worker rather than that of the layman. The case of the governing body of one South Carolina district which, according to one of its supervisors: " . . . took the [district] plan written up by the Soil Conservation Service and tore it all to pieces," is the exception that proves the average.[31]

It once was the common practice for state or district Service personnel to prepare a general preliminary draft of the program and work plan, which farmer supervisors were to review, criticize, and change to conform with farmer thinking. Supervisors and district conservationists, when questioned concerning the preparation of the programs and work plans of districts where a preliminary draft is made by technicians, most frequently give the following characterizations:

---

[31] Minutes, Meeting of South Carolina Association of Soil Conservation Districts Supervisors, Columbia, January 18, 19, 1945, p. 8.

The SCS boys prepared a rough draft and then gave it to us supervisors for our criticisms. We thought it was pretty good as it stood.

Or

Well, the bulk of the work is usually done by our men. The supervisors, of course, have ample opportunity to give their ideas and suggestions. Yes, they have often been reluctant to make any changes.

Or

The lead in preparing these documents has been taken by the Soil Conservation Service and the Extension.

Or

The supervisors did offer their suggestions but were content to give the responsibility for drafting the documents to Service men.

Or

We read over and signed the document. It seemed to suit our purpose.

Because technician preparation of even a preliminary draft was discouraging supervisor participation, the Service in recent years has been strongly emphasizing that the technicians are not to prepare even a rough draft of the work plan without the active participation of the supervisors. As early as 1939, J. Phil Campbell, the Chief of the Division of Cooperative Relations, SCS, explained:

This [the writing of programs and work plans by SCS personnel] may be excused at the start of a new program, but it's wrong and I'll admit it freely. I can only say that we are making every possible effort to eliminate this kind of thing and to instruct our technical men in their proper responsibilities.[32]

No worthwhile estimates can be made concerning the degree of farmer participation in supervisors-technician meetings for preparing the district program and work plan. Even within a state where the same techniques for assisting districts in preparing their plans are used in every district, farmer participation varies from district to district. "We have met with varying degrees of success in getting active farmer participation," the assistant state conservationist from Iowa reported. "Quite a number of district commissioners do have a large share in preparing these documents." He cited one particular district whose meetings for preparing its program and work plan were especially good. Some of the farmers were dissatisfied with the material which was to be included in these documents at the first meeting. Another meeting was called. One farmer who had objected to

---

[32] "The Coordination of Extension and Soil Conservation Service Programs in Soil Conservation Districts," address before New Mexico State Extension Conference, January 26, 1939, p. 4.

the thinking expressed at the original meeting was working on it during the intervening month.

The writer observed a meeting held to develop a program and work plan in one Wisconsin district, where despite the continuous efforts of the Service workers, extension conservationist, and the county agent to get their participation, the supervisors could not be persuaded appreciably to contribute information or opinions. Yet in another Wisconsin district, where the same techniques were used, the development of the program was largely taken over by the farmers.

The fact that the supervisors have not participated as actively as desirable in developing their district program and work plan does not necessarily mean that they do not participate in the determination of district policies. The failure of governing bodies generally to take a real part in the development of these policy documents is chiefly due to their light regard for these documents. Often when asked concerning the preparation of such documents, they have apparently almost forgotten these written policies exist. Their subsequent policy decisions made in their meetings as a board, usually are taken without regard for conformity to the original formal documents. In carrying on the routine administrative work of the district, supervisors frequently override the policies of the work plan.

Review of Farm Plans

The reviewing of complete farm plans has been the activity of governing bodies which could most critically affect district policy in its relations with farmer cooperators. It was the crucial spot in determining whether SCS standards for minimum conservation treatments were to prevail in the district. Regardless of whether minimum standards for determining the adequacy of each farm plan were laid down in the district work plan, the supervisors' determination of the adequacy of each individual farm plan, which they reviewed, set the policy of the district. The failure of a governing body to give a real review to farm plans was in itself a determination to accept SCS technicians' judgments on what was an acceptable basis for assisting a farmer.

Under the old procedure, all farmer-district agreements were signed by at least one member of the district's governing body, after reviewing the plan the technician had prepared. But the thoroughness of review which supervisors actually gave farm plans varied widely. At the low end of the activity scale were perhaps a fourth of the district governing bodies. These did little more than attach their signatures to the agreements. The district conservationist for one midwestern district described his difficulty in getting a supervisor into the office merely to sign the farm plans. "All the while he was signing, the supervisor kept complaining that he wished he had a rubber stamp."

The majority of district boards generally gave only cursory attention to those plans which had the approval of both the technician and the farmer. Their function generally was to judge the acceptability to the district of farm plans whose adequacy was questioned by the technician.

As a supervisor from one southern district explained: "When he [the SCS farm planner] gives me a couple of farm plans to sign, he gives me his idea of how good the plans are. He might say: 'Well, we really fixed this farmer up a good plan; but this other plan is just so much paper, because the farmer wasn't willing to accept anything.' "

The common attitude of supervisors toward reviewing farm plans was voiced in the discussion among Nebraska supervisors at one of their state meetings. "Any agreement that had the OK of the technician, then it should be OK," declared a supervisor from the Valley County District. "If they OK it, what more can we do?" To which another supervisor added:

They [the supervisors] want to approve the plans that the technician has worked out and recommended. If there is a plan where the technician isn't satisfied, the supervisors would be glad to turn that kind of plan down. If it is a thing that the farmer wants and is satisfactory to the technician, then we supervisors should approve it without too much discussion. If it is a plan that the technician isn't too well satisfied with, then the supervisors and technicians should discuss it and if it does not meet with their approval, then it should be turned down.[33]

Supervisors, however, have not necessarily accepted the views of the technician in a disagreement between a technician and a farmer. Their inclination has been to follow a technique of gradually persuading a farmer to accept a complete plan by letting him have the sample of the single practice he desires. As a supervisor from the Sugarloaf District, Nebraska, explained:

Oftentimes we have a disagreement between the technicians and farmers and then the supervisors intervene. We find if the farmer isn't satisfied, if he will come into the meeting, if he won't agree to all of

---

[33] Proceedings, Nebraska Supervisors Association, *op. cit.,* p. 25.

the plan, there is a phase to which he will agree and on which he goes ahead. Then he wants the next one. A little education often gets the job done where arguing wouldn't work.[34]

Supervisors only infrequently turned down a farm plan. This is the consensus of all state and district conservationists interviewed. When Nebraska supervisors were specifically asked if they had ever disapproved a plan, only two supervisors reported affirmatively. These were plans which called for nothing but a dam. "We turned down a farm plan one time. A fellow wanted a dam, nothing more. He was pretty sore but in about two years he got the dam, but did the soil conservation work first." Another supervisor added that he knew of one other district that turned down an agreement.

Governing bodies generally have not given a real review to each farm plan for two reasons. As farmers with full time jobs upon their land, they have not felt that they could give to the district the hours necessary for carefully reviewing plans. Nor have they often felt themselves competent to take issue with their technicians. The supervisor, in theory, was to judge a farm plan from the farmer's standpoint. In fact, supervisors have frequently made such judgments. For example, the district conservationist for one Wisconsin district reported that supervisors there were quite active in suggesting changes in farm plans — not in relation to what treatments the land needed, but in their knowledge of what could be expected of individual farmers.

Supervisors, particularly in the larger districts, often did not know farmers and their farms well enough to make a decision upon each plan. For most farms in their district, they did not feel competent to take a stand against a plan which the farmer accepted and was satisfactory to the technician. Their attitude commonly has beeen: "We're not in a position to judge a plan unless we know the farmer." As a supervisor in one of the large Alabama districts stated: "I can't know all the farms in my county, and, after all, the farm planner and the farmer are bound to know more about what is a good plan for a particular farm than I could know by reviewing it."

At the high end of the activity scale has been a minority of district boards which made a conscientious effort to examine and appraise farm plans regardless of their approval by the technicians. For example, the East Goodhue District, Minnesota, reported:

---

[34] *Ibid.*, p. 20.

Fig. 10 — Terraces, strip crops, and contour cultivation for soil and water conservation in Texas.

Fig. 11 — Terrace construction with disc plow and tractor.

"At these meetings we follow our technicians' work as it is being applied on the farms. This is especially true of our new agreements which are gone over and discussed before they get our official approval." In the Sugarloaf District, Nebraska, a supervisor reported: "We take every plan before all the supervisors and they are discussed, analyzed and passed on by all of us. It is not left to one man's judgment."

Generally the boards which attempted to review the planning work of the technicians devised various means for getting the reviewing job down to a manageable size. The most common device was to divide the district into geographic areas and to assign to each supervisor the responsibility of studying the plans from his specific area.

The Thomas Jefferson District, one of the stronger districts in Virginia whose supervisors reportedly gave a real review to farm plans, assigned the reviewing of the farm plans for each county to the supervisor from that county. A Kansas supervisor reported that his board divided the agreements so that each supervisor reviewed those for his part of the district. When a supervisor had any doubts about one, the whole board discussed and passed upon the plan.

Another device used to cut the task of reviewing farm plans to a manageable size was the selection of only a portion of the reports for careful review. As examples, a Wyoming district selected a representative sample of the agreements for thorough review. Supervisors of a West Virginia district reviewed only those plans involving some machinery problem. They were particularly interested in weighing the balance between what the farmer and the district agreed to do. Supervisors of an Illinois district developed the procedure of day meetings on Saturday, when new cooperators themselves presented the plans they had developed. In this manner the farmer was given a positive opportunity to voice any dissatisfaction he might have with his plan.

Under the present three-stage planning procedure, the district, through one or more of its supervisors, signs an agreement with a farmer before any plan has been made for his farm. No further agreement is signed as the farmer progresses into the advanced stage or when he receives and accepts his basic plan. Thus supervisors have lost one of their functions which was regarded as critical in the maintenance of a high level of district conservation performance. The balance between supervisors and technicians in the setting of district conservation standards in reality did not shift appreciably to the technicians because of this change. In the first place, supervisors have always leaned towards the belief that any combination of practices a farmer was willing to accept was a suitable basis for extending district assistance. Secondly, the actual reviewing of farm plans by supervisors was too scattered to make for a real control by supervisors over district standards. Finally, under the revised procedure, supervisors can, if they will, make determinations upon the adequacy of contemplated practices as a basis for giving district assistance.

Under the procedure for extending SCS technical assistance to clients of the ACP program, the technician, when he makes his first visit to a farmer, is to point out the advantages of becoming a cooperator in the district program. That is, he is to attempt to persuade him to sign a farmer-district agreement. But the district supervisors also must sign the agreement before it is in force. Although the drive is on to get universal coverage in the district program, regional SCS officials have recently indicated that district conservationists are reporting frequent instances of district supervisors considering it useless to sign agreements with certain farmers because of the likelihood that those farmers will never carry out a real conservation program.

If district supervisors take an active part in the preparation of the technician's schedules for servicing farmers, they can exercise some review over the adequacy of contemplated conservation work. They can set priorities for assistance to individual farmers on the basis of which practices are most needed, which ones will result in the most lasting conservation returns, how well contemplated practices fit into a rounded conservation program for the farm, and so on. Region I is now attempting to formalize this supervisor reviewing function through a procedure for the issuance by district boards of "work orders." Before the technician renders assistance to a cooperator the technician is to have a work order from the supervisors. Supervisors, through the work order, will be making decisions not only on the rendering of technical assistance, but upon the amount and kind of planting stock with which a farmer should be supplied, and upon the provision of necessary machinery. Of course a farmer who is refused assistance through the district program can sometimes obtain that assistance on the basis of his being an ACP client. However, the SCS technician determines the technical adequacy and suitability of the contemplated ACP practice, and it is not likely that the technician's standards will be lower than those of the supervisors.

Supervision of Equipment

The administrative tasks which supervisors have most frequently shifted over to the SCS technicians are the management of district equipment and the distribution of materials. Most supervisors feel that they cannot spare the hours necessary for the routing and supervision of equipment. They see the technician, in his job of aiding in the application of practices, as being in a strategic position for routing and keeping track of equipment and issuing conservation materials. So commonly have supervisors thrown these jobs upon the technicians, that each year thousands of man hours are diverted from the technical work of farm planning and directing the application of practices.

Preparation of Annual Report

Preparation of the annual report is not an activity which bears directly upon district policies in the sense that board meetings or administrative work, such as reviewing plans, do. Yet supervisors, in the annual report, have a potential instrument for broadly influencing district policy. In the first place, the annual report gives district governing bodies an organized channel for getting their reactions to Service policies up to the regional and national levels. For example, district boards widely used their 1951 annual reports to voice their dissatisfaction with, and fear of, the arrangement for extending SCS technical assistance to non-district cooperators. This supervisor reaction, as expressed in the annual reports, was channeled on up to Secretary Brannan. Secondly, through the annual report, supervisors have a means of so influencing popular opinion in the district that further district actions may be undertaken. Finally, in reviewing district problems, needs, and progress, and in disciplining their thinking sufficiently to summarize and appraise district policies and operations, supervisors may develop greater competency and willingness to formulate future district policies. In reviewing past district activity, supervisors frequently have developed opinions upon suitable courses for future district activity.

The Soil Conservation Service has exerted more pressure upon district boards to draft their own annual reports than to perform any other activity. The chief of operations of the Service expressed the viewpoint of the Service to Nebraska supervisors in their annual meeting:

The Annual Report is the responsibility of the supervisors. It is their job and they should decide what goes into it because they are the ones who are telling, in that annual report, what their district has done during the year. It is the place of the technicians to help by furnishing figures and doing any of the helper type of work that needs to be done. But, I do believe the report is the opportunity of the supervisors to tell in their own way what they have done and what their district has done during the year. For my part, the State Committee, and the Soil Conservation Service, we would rather feel that the supervisors' report is a story told by the supervisors themselves as to what they have done during the year. We know that you men are busy, but we would like to see you take the time to make the annual report.[35]

Supervisors, on the other hand, generally are quite reluctant to take over such a job. Writing in so organized and formal a fashion is an unfamiliar task. They feel they do not have the technique or language facility. As a supervisor in the Great Plains put it: "Since most of us supervisors haven't got the $5 or $10 words, we let the technicians do the writing." Moreover, it is a task which farmers see as particularly time consuming. The admonition of one of his fellow supervisors reveals that this is a consideration in their thinking: "Supervisors should spend time with it even if they don't get paid."

In the early years of the conservation program, district reports were written almost exclusively by SCS district personnel. Frequently no effort was made to disguise the fact that the report was technician written. For example, the supervisors were commonly alluded to in the third person. As a result of Service insistence, in recent years, that its field staff take no responsibility for the annual report, there has been a trend toward supervisor written reports. An examination of district reports by years reveals for each successive year an increasingly large number of reports whose tone and language is that of farmers, rather than technicians.

The year 1943 marked the sharp turning point toward the writing of reports by supervisors. State and district conservationists are in agreement that the supervisors now are having a much greater share in preparing annual reports. As a state conservationist in the South put it: "Supervisors have been goaded into doing most of it." At least a fourth of the district boards now are writing their own annual reports, and probably more than half of the remaining districts are using a procedure for reviewing reports which gives them ample opportunity to criticize and revise the preliminary technician prepared draft. In many districts the board holds one or more preliminary meetings to discuss and suggest to

---

[35] Proceedings, Nebraska Supervisors Association, *op. cit.*, p. 21.

the technicians the information which is to go into the report. After the preliminary draft is prepared, another meeting is devoted to reviewing the report.

REVIEW AND CONTROL OF DISTRICT ACTIVITY

Review and control of district policy and operation — the final phase in an administrative process — is interwoven with the formulation and execution of district policies. For supervisors to have enough knowledge of their district's problems to review and control district activity, they need to participate in the formulation and execution of district policies. In carrying on the routing of machinery and the issuing of planting stock, for example, supervisors gain an overview of the work to be accomplished, plans for application, sufficiency of materials and equipment on hand, and rate of accomplishment. This information equips them to make an intelligent decision on the balancing of planning with application work. By reviewing farm plans and talking with farmers concerning their plans, supervisors get an appreciation of farmer economic needs versus technical conservation requirements. This is a necessary basis for taking any stand on the minimum conservation treatments held necessary by technicians.

District administrations are beginning to develop two general types of supervisor review activities which, if carried on systematically, would combine to give governing boards a good picture of the effectiveness of district operations. The first type of supervisor review is a kind of independent field checking with farmer cooperators. The objective is not only to discover farmer attitudes toward the conservation work and the nature of their relationships with the technicians, but also to check upon the degree to which farmers are carrying out their commitments. Supervisor visits also serve as a means of encouraging farmers to carry out their commitments to apply and maintain agreed upon conservation measures.

Supervisors in many of the stronger district boards are now systematically attempting to spend a day or two at regular intervals visiting farmer cooperators. As an illustration, the Marshall-Putnam District, Illinois, reports:

During the month of June the directors made calls on fifteen farm plan holders. The intention was to learn if the cooperators felt satisfied with their plans and what their current reaction was toward our Soil Conservation Program. Those called upon seemed quite pleased. Most all of them felt the farm plans had been a material aid, though several plans appeared in need of some revision. Many took pride in showing improvements in their farms due principally to suggestions made by Soil Conservation Technicians. . . .

The directors have felt that there was a two-fold gain from these visits. First, it gave the directors further evidence of the type of work accomplished by the technicians on varied types of farms, and the direct reaction of cooperators to the Soil Conservation District's work. Second, it indicated a need for periodic check-ups on all farm plans to encourage their revisions to meet operational changes so frequently occurring on all farms.

In the Piedmont District, Alabama, the state conservationist reported that: "Each supervisor during the year spent one or more days studying the work which has been done under the district's program in his home county. He visited sections of the county that were not frequently visited by him." In the Benton County District, Arkansas, each supervisor, after visiting farmers in his community, reported on the accomplishments and attitudes in his particular area in a section of the annual report called "Personal Views of the Supervisors of their Respective Communities." District boards frequently record in their annual reports that the supervisors attempt to visit the farmer cooperators in their own communities at least once a year.

The second general type of supervisor review of district activity is the systematic reporting to supervisors by technicians on the work they have been doing. In New York, as an illustration, technicians in several of the districts are preparing a summary of accomplishments for each directors' meeting. This type of technician reporting is probably being carried on, in a less organized fashion, in most of the districts.

Supervisors, of course, have no authority to remove a conservation technician who in their view is unsatisfactorily performing his duties, or who ignores their decisions. However, the Service, from the national office down to the district conservationist, has followed a consistent policy of attempting to meet supervisor wishes upon Service personnel within a district. District conservationists in several states explained that their work unit conservationists had to get along with the supervisors or that they would see to their transfer. The assistant state conservationist in one southern state explained that supervisors are consulted before placing SCS technicians in a district. He reported two instances of transfers being made at supervisors' suggestion.

District boards themselves generally have realized their strategic position in their relations with local SCS personnel. They perceive that a threat to resign is sufficient to bring about almost any personnel change they may indicate. In a southwestern state, the state conservationist reports that several districts have requested the removal of unsatisfactory district personnel. In a district in a far western state where the district conservationist did not carry out the decision of the board concerning priorities of jobs and localities for use of equipment, the board threatened to resign unless the conservationist was removed. The state office, however, was already acting to secure his transfer. When a Negro technician was sent into the Southside District, Virginia, the supervisors declared, in their 1942 annual report:

> We feel that the administrative policies between the Department of Agriculture and the Board of Supervisors is not quite clear. We believe the future of the Board of Supervisors is uncertain unless more of the responsibility of the district is assumed by the Board of Supervisors and more of its policies determined by the board. In other words, we believe that the Board of Supervisors should be consulted before new policies are inaugurated. We do not wish to be finding fault but to be specific, we do not think that Negro technicians should have been sent into our district without consulting us. We do not object to the Negro technicians as such, but we think we should have known about their appointment to this district before it was done.

That district administration has not yet sufficiently become supervisor administration is a commonly accepted fact. Supervisors generally are not yet fully carrying their governing responsibilities — either in determining policies or in the routine management work of the district. Even the stronger district boards, in their management activities, depend heavily upon the professional workers. Perhaps the most encouraging dimension in supervisor administration is that, within so brief a period as fifteen years, so much progress has been made in developing processes, organizational devices, and techniques for a productive operational merging of the skills of the conservation technician and the farmer supervisor. The resulting cross-fertilization of national and local experiences promises increasingly to produce a sounder and better proportioned approach to conservation activity than if either technicians or farmers were attempting to go it alone.

CHAPTER 5

Increasing Supervisors' Role in District Administration

The activitity of farmer supervisors in district government has increased in the fifteen years of the district's existence, according to many state conservationists' reports. This progress has not come about through age alone. In many of the recently created districts, supervisors are immediately shouldering a larger share of the management work than supervisors in the earlier districts had at first assumed. This contrast indicates that, over the fifteen-year period, a variety of devices and techniques has been developed which lead supervisors into more active management of their districts. The observation of the Texas state conservationist is typical: "It is noticeable that supervisors in the newer districts are assuming their responsibilities with a greater degree of understanding and interest than was true earlier in the history of the districts."

The drive for conserving the nation's rural lands through the soil conservation district was not due to spontaneous local impulse. Rather it was the product of the preconceived idea of national and state governments that soil conservation could best be achieved through local people organized into units of local government. Therefore, federal and state agricultural agencies have felt it their responsibility to aid the districts in becoming genuine local, going concerns. The chief of the Division of States Relations was voicing the official SCS opinion when he declared that:

If districts are to be organizations of the people, for the people, and run by the people, the district supervisors must somehow assume full responsibility for their administration. Soil Conservation Districts will be unable to survive as such unless ways and means are found whereby supervisors can carry this responsibility.[1]

As the district has matured, supervisors themselves have organized into state associations which also share in the responsibility for increasing supervisor management of district affairs. Thus, the staffs of the Soil Conservation Service and Extension Services — acting both individually and cooperatively through the state advisory committee and extension soil conservationists[2] — the state soil conservation committee, and the national and state district supervisors associations have joined in a common effort to create devices and techniques for bringing about active supervisor government.

The quite general failure of supervisors to assume their full responsibilities in governing their districts arises from two causes. The first, and probably the most important, is the nonacceptance of district management activities by farmer supervisors. The second is the tendency of Service technicians to overdominate the work of the districts. As the Region III director has pointed out: "SCS personnel too often assume the functions of the governing body, not distinguishing between administration and advisory assistance."[3]

STIMULATING SUPERVISOR INTEREST

The techniques and devices for increasing supervisor willingness and competence to manage district affairs are closely intertwined because: (1) Supervisor understanding of the problems and work of the district, which makes for competency, also increases supervisor appreciation of the need for devoting time to district affairs. (2) The feeling of capacity for managing the district, which grows out of competency, increases supervisor willingness to accept management responsibilities. (3) Many of the media for increasing supervisor competence also develop a greater supervisor interest in working for the district. The effort to separate the techniques for developing supervisor willingness to carry on the management work of the district from those for increasing capacity to do so makes for an unrealistic classification. Yet such a breakdown is expedient for purposes of analysis.

---

[1] Ivan L. Hobson, "Some Business Aspects of Soil Conservation Districts," statement presented at the annual meeting of Supervisors of Soil Conservation Districts in Colorado, Denver, October 11, 1940, p. 7.

[2] The extension soil conservationist is cooperatively employed by SCS and the State Extension Service.

[3] "A Guide to Service Participation in Cooperative Activities in Soil Conservation," *op. cit.*, p. 7.

Perhaps the most critical problem in developing farmer-citizen administration of a public agricultural activity is creating the will to donate limited free time to the community's work. If willingness to serve is present in a supervisor, he usually with experience becomes competent in managing district affairs.

Need for Suitable Supervisor Personnel

Although a variety of techniques has been used effectively to create supervisor interest in conservation, the general feeling of professional agricultural workers is that it is most desirable that there be originally present in a supervisor the raw material of some basic willingness to lead in conservation work. "Getting supervisors with a disposition to serve is one of the most important factors in developing strong supervisor administration," pointed out an Extension-SCS conservationist, from his close observations of district administrations.

ORIGINAL INTEREST IN CONSERVATION

State and district conservationists repeatedly have observed that, although much can be done to increase supervisor willingness to serve in district work, supervisors with a real original interest in conserving their community's soil generally have developed into the strongest, most competent supervisors. As a midwestern state conservationist put it:

> To a large extent this simmers down to the fact that good supervisors, who are interested in doing a job, have improved with experience, while those who did not ever make any contribution did not deteriorate to any extent.

Sometimes "strong" supervisors are more effective than a professional worker in arousing the interest of their fellows. The Wisconsin conservationist observed:

> We could cite several other Districts that have improved their administration by virtue of one or two individuals who are continually developing. These men have come to the fore, exerted leadership and have, in a way, towed along other members of the governing bodies. Seemingly, this is a reverse of the "rotten apple" theory.

In general, the Wisconsin procedure of using the members of the agricultural committee of the county board of supervisors as district supervisors reveals the desirability of securing, as supervisors, farmers with a real will to serve in a community conservation effort. The Wisconsin method of selecting supervisors has sometimes brought into district administration farmers with no real interest in the work of the district.

The Wisconsin experience nicely points up both the advantages and disadvantages of a special district for conservation administration in comparison to working through regular county government. It has been argued that in the arduous, pioneer task of organizing a community to save its soil, there is needed a special local group which sees the need for expending unusual energy upon the task. County government, so the argument runs, is often so oriented towards the traditional local governmental functions that it is easier to create a new unit of government than to attempt to reorient county government and galvanize it into new types of public action. This need for vigorous administration and promotional zeal in a new governmental activity is one of the most common reasons given for creating special districts. In the case of the conservation district, the further confusing of the multiplicity of local government by the addition of another unit is compensated for, in part at least, by the new process of integrating the efforts of national and local units in a common task.

The great potential of the Wisconsin system, which uses the county board's agricultural committee for administering a variety of rural programs, lies in the fact that it provides mechanical opportunities for coordinating all agricultural work and tieing it into over-all county government. Since soil conservation is only one phase of the total rural government in a county, the Wisconsin system cannot be judged solely on the basis of supervisor enthusiasm for conservation work. The need for coordinated program administration in the county might well overbalance any lack of conservation zeal shown by the Wisconsin supervisors in comparison with supervisors in sister states who have only the single task of conservation administration.

Fifteen years of experience is not long as government institutions go, and no one can say with finality that there is any one best form of organizing conservation activity. It is therefore fortunate that the Wisconsin experiment is going on alongside the standard district arrangement in other states. Out of such comparative experiences a compromise arrangement may be discovered which will meet the objection of government students to the splintering effect of special districts, and at the same time afford the vigorous administration which conservationists feel is imperative.

The need for obtaining farmer supervisors with a genuine willingness to devote their energies to a community soil conserving program does not preclude the election of supervisors. The very willingness of a farmer to stand for election as a district supervisor is some indication of his interest in the program. Moreover, as the Service's field staff readily agrees, even the hand-picking of supervisors by professional agricultural workers in the county often results in the selection of supervisors with little real interest in conservation.

The corollary to the original securing of farmer supervisors with an interest in the district's work is the removal of those supervisors who, after having had sufficient opportunity to develop, remain inactive in district administration. There has been too great a tendency to permit supervisors to remain in their posts indefinitely, regardless of whether they are participating in district work. But several state conservationists have cited the removal of inactive supervisors as a symptom of strengthening supervisor administration. To illustrate, the state conservationist in a southwestern state reports that active supervisors have in a number of instances requested the resignation of a fellow board member who for various reasons could not properly serve. In one Illinois district the directors asked an uncooperative member to resign. In Maryland, the districts in one work group have adopted a policy of annually electing district officers. In one district it is reported that a ". . . dormant treasurer was replaced by one who seems to be willing to accept the full responsibility of the office."

SUFFICIENT TIME FOR DISTRICT WORK

Perhaps the most basic obstacle to developing active supervisor government is the limited free time which the farmer can spare, from the business of making a living, for public tasks. As was discovered in the effort to secure farmer participation in the Land Use Planning program, the farmers who are the more willing to shoulder new activities in soil conservation are generally those men already busiest in organized group and community activities — that is, the "perennial participators," the "Extension farmers," the Farm Bureau or Grange leaders, or PMA committeemen. This phenomenon has resulted not only from their prominence and leadership position in their communities, which makes them known to the county agent and other professional workers. It also grows out of the fact that the farmers who have not been participating in organized agricultural activities — either because of habit patterns of nonparticipation or for economic and social reasons — are reluctant to accept such public responsibilities, even when real effort is made to get their participation.[4]

Whatever the causes may be, district administration, it is generally agreed, is not to any large extent bringing into itself fresh farmer personnel not already carrying other public and group responsibilities. Therefore, although the Region V director may speak of the need for dispelling erroneous ideas that supervisors are too busy to be bothered, there is a central problem here for which no real solution has been found.[5] The remarkable thing to many who have observed district administration is that supervisors have given so freely of their time and energy to make the districts move.

Incentive Techniques for Arousing Supervisor Interest

Despite the fact that an original interest in working for community soil conservation is sometimes a prerequisite for the maturing of an active, competent supervisor, and that farmer supervisors have only limited free time to devote to district work, fifteen years of experience in district administration have demonstrated that supervisor activity can be increased through various incentive techniques.

The techniques and devices employed to create in supervisors such an interest in conservation that they will devote maximum energy to district work must, in general, touch two mainsprings in psychological motivation: (1) Supervisors must be made aware of the importance of conservation to the welfare of their community. (2) Their work in the public conservation effort must in itself be a satisfying experience.

CREATING SUPERVISOR UNDERSTANDING OF CONSERVATION NEEDS

Supervisor administration will not improve with age, the Soil Conservation Service has repeatedly stressed, unless methods are found for giving supervisors a vision of the purpose of district organization.

During the educational period, when the organization of a district is being sought, supervisors, usually participants in the organization movement, receive a rather intensive indoctrination in the need for community conservation. SCS and Extension

---

[4] Ellen S. Parks, "Experiment in the Democratic Planning of Public Agricultural Activities," Ph.D. Thesis, Wisconsin, 1947, pp. 46–54.

[5] Memorandum from A. E. McClymonds, to All Ranking Field Personnel, "District Conservationists and Their Relationships with District Supervisors," SCS Region V, Memorandum No. 409.

Services have been leaders in developing visual aids and printed publicity methods for reporting to the public upon the necessity for public action. Their publicity is effectively used during the organization of a district. Tours or visits to areas within the district where erosion damage is particularly serious are customary. The holding of meetings at which specialists from the state college or a representative of the state soil conservation committee speak upon particular erosion problems in the community is common practice.

Indoctrination of both supervisors and farmers in the importance of the district is looked upon by the SCS staff as a continuous process which carries over into district operations. Much thought has been given to the problem of integrating the educational work of the district, for which the state Extension Service is responsible, into the daily operations of the district. SCS largely depends, however, upon the district conservationist to convince supervisors of the community's stake in conservation work. For example, the Region V director has suggested to district staffs that they help the district supervisors understand the importance of the job to be done by pointing out that:

> The work of the district may eventually have material effect on the value of all real estate in the district. For example, if there are 300,000 acres in the district and the average value is $25.00 per acre, the real estate valuation of the district is seven and one-half million dollars. Such a valuable resource is worth saving. . . . Be sure they know how erosion lowers and how conservation raises real estate values. Be sure they have the facts about local examples of increased yields resulting from conservation practices.[6]

In general, supervisor perception of the importance of conservation can be depended upon to grow with the supervisors' growing understanding of the problems and operation of the district.

However clearly district supervisors may see their community's need for controlling soil erosion, unless their participation in district administration is a satisfying, rewarding experience, supervisors will not long remain active. Commonly, the factors which make supervisors competent to handle the administration of the district are those which create farmer satisfaction in carrying out their management activities. But there are additional devices for

---

[6] "District Conservationists and Their Relationships with District Supervisors," *op. cit.*, pp. 1, 2.

arousing supervisor interest in their work which are largely in the nature of incentive techniques.

MAKING MANAGEMENT WORK SATISFYING

A feeling of concrete accomplishment is one of the most effective incentives for devoting time and energy to any chore. District administration can be so organized that it gives supervisors this feeling.

District "Action" Programs

One incentive factor is the development of one or more vigorous *action* programs by the district. Cause and effect cannot always be distinguished, but district conservationists agree that there is a noticeable correlation between districts with strong action programs and strong supervisor participation in district activity. Apparently a real action program, which shows in concrete accomplishments the work of the district, aids in creating stronger governing bodies. For instance, in one district in the Midwest which had no active conservation program, the board chairman, tapping the district conservationist upon the shoulder, explained: "We leave all the work to these boys." On the other hand, supervisors of the Chenango County District, New York, which carries on several vigorous action activities declared in an annual report:

> The directors want to make themselves clear; the Soil Conservation Service does not manage our affairs. The Chenango County Board of Supervisors appoint five men to do that job and we can make agreements with any agency we see fit to get the job done quickly, efficiently and as cheaply as possible.

It has been noticeable that in the districts which have been organizing group facility programs, such as drainage and irrigation, supervisors have usually been actively controlling district affairs. The Pavillion District, Wyoming, is a notable example of the relationship between group facility programs and supervisor interest. A vigorous equipment program has been observed by Service personnel to be particularly effective in arousing supervisor interest in district management. A New England state conservationist has stated:

> Generally speaking, the interest of Supervisors is directly related to the amount of equipment the District has, either of its own or that it has been able to obtain through contractors. . . . The Supervisors in Districts that have been without equipment for some time tend to be somewhat discouraged with the progress of their program.

In some western districts it has been said that supervisor concentration upon machinery for the district program has perhaps weakened other phases of the program, such as education. It also has been frequently observed that in districts which have entered into the supply business — that is the purchasing and selling of seeds, planting stocks, and other conservation material such as cement, fencing, dynamite — the governing bodies are commonly running their districts.

Out of its observations of district administrations and reports from its district staffs, the SCS Region III office has concluded that action programs are incentives to supervisor activity. As early as 1943, it recommended to its district personnel:

> Promote some *action* activity under the district program. Anything that will show progress and action will help to hold interest.
>
> Such activities include the operation of special equipment, special demonstrations, drainage, wildlife projects, cooperative wood marketing, special courses on conservation in public schools and vocational agriculture departments, where the members of the governing body appear before classes and talk about the conservation program on their own farms, contour plowing contests, terrace construction contests, planting bees, etc.[7]

District's Possession of Funds

Out of the development of the various types of action programs sometimes come substantial cash balances. Possession of district funds gives supervisors not only a feeling of the significance of their jobs, but also a sense of district independence. This stimulates supervisor initiative and responsibility in managing district affairs. The relationship between the possession of funds and the strength of supervisor administration has been remarked by those close to district operations in various sections of the country. For example, the county agent and the Service technicians in one Utah district expressed the opinion that the possession of funds by that district has given supervisors a greater feeling of responsibility. A supervisor in a South Carolina district declared: "The District needs funds of its own so supervisors can do more, feel more responsibility and have more influence." This point has been well illustrated in Iowa, where district commissioners almost overnight responded to the state appropriation in 1949 as if they had been given a shot in the arm. Region III emphasizes the value of the possession of district funds as an incentive device:

---

[7] "Working with District Governing Bodies," SCS Region III Memorandum, p. 8.

Fig. 12 — Supervisors in some districts systematically check conservation plans with farmer cooperators.

Fig. 13 — Supervisors should understand the place of such practices as contour farming in a balanced conservation program.

Provide funds to be handled by the governing body. This may be done through state or local appropriations, or through profits from some enterprise appropriate to the district program. Handling money gives a sense of responsibility.[8]

Supervisor Performance of Concrete Tasks

Another device for creating a sense of accomplishment is the performance of concrete tasks by supervisors. This is an effective incentive technique despite the prevailing supervisor reluctance to carry out the routine, ministerial tasks in district administration. For district conservationists observe that when supervisors are persuaded to perform some concrete jobs their interest in district administration has been further stimulated.

Concrete activities which bring supervisors into personal contact with the district's farmers are particularly effective. Aiding in the preparation of one or two farm plans each year, going over the technician's plan with the farmer himself, and paying follow-up calls on farmers engaged in carrying out their plans stimulate both farmer and supervisor interest in conservation work. Supervisors frequently are urged by the state conservation committee, Service personnel, and the Extension conservationist to spend at least one day a month visiting district farmers. The Michigan state conservationist reports that there is developing in many Michigan districts the practice of supervisors participating in the preparation of a scattering of farm plans each year. In the Allegany County District, New York, supervisors have made monthly inspections of work being done on farms.

Conducting farmer group meetings, meeting with other organized groups in the community, participating in district tours to problem conservation areas or to noteworthy conservation accomplishments, and carrying out demonstrations are also tasks which leave a sense of concrete accomplishment. Region III suggests that supervisors and other local people should carry on demonstrations in running contour lines, terrace lines, laying out strips, etc.[9]

Dividing the total administrative work of the district into manageable portions and specifically giving each supervisor responsibility for certain phases of district activity not only permits more effective supervisor management of the district's program, but it also increases supervisor will to carry on the district's work.

---

[8] *Ibid.,* p. 8.
[9] "Procedure for Guidance in Cooperating with Soil Conservation Districts," *op. cit.,* p. 8.

Such breakdowns permit supervisors to get their teeth into the work and feel that they have specific tasks suited to their available time and competence. If work assignments can be fitted to the particular interests of a supervisor, the provision of definite duties is particularly effective. The Region III office explains that "each man usually has a special interest in some part of the program. By working on this special interest it is possible to develop that individual into an effective leader for the activity." It relates, as a case in point:

> One district supervisor we know about never showed much interest — in fact, he rarely attended the meetings of the board. Finally the district decided to open a marl pit and to buy a dragline. The district conservationist was about to inspect a dragline which was for sale and to make a report on its condition and value. Knowing that this supervisor was quite well informed on machinery and interested in its operation, the district conservationist invited him to go along to determine the condition of the machine. As a result, this man has become one of the most active supervisors on the board and is in charge of equipment for the district.[10]

Purposeful Sessions of District Boards

Since the prevailing attitude of supervisors has been that almost all their responsibilities can be discharged during their regular board meetings, it is here that supervisor interest in performing further concrete tasks must be awakened. It is of prime importance that such meetings leave supervisors with a sense of accomplishment. "No one likes to go to a meeting that drags out, has no order, and accomplishes nothing. Well planned and well conducted meetings will do much to bring people back to subsequent ones," explains the Region III office.[11]

Meetings should always have a purpose — definite business which should be taken care of by the supervisors. Supervisors should be confronted with definite problems and encouraged to make their own decisions upon each problem. The reaction of an Oklahoma supervisor to his board's lack of business is revealing. He explained that he would ". . . have to quit going unless there was more to do." His private business needed him. But he was ready to shoulder his part, if it was necessary.

The Region V director warns his district staffs: "Do not encourage district supervisors to hold meetings, either of the governing body or in a community, unless business, subject mat-

---

[10] "Working with District Governing Bodies," *op. cit.*, pp. 7, 8.
[11] *Ibid.*, p. 3.

ter, or operations work of sufficient importance warrants." [12] One Tennessee district conservationist, who is alert to the need for developing supervisor administration, explains that he is always at pains to see that the chairmen of the boards in his area have worked up enough business for each supervisor meeting. He lists the following as typical problems considered in board meetings:

(1) Problems relating to equipment for doing conservation work, such as contracts, rates to be charged, etc.
(2) Priority of areas to be worked.
(3) Selection of delegate to state association meeting.
(4) Methods of procuring needed seeds.
(5) Methods of securing applications.

District technicians are being continually exhorted by the Service staff to bring their problems with supporting facts to the board itself. The Washington office urges district technicians to:

Bring to the attention of the supervisors opportunities for taking important steps and avoid doing for supervisors those things that they should do or cause to be done by others. It is good service to help many people do important things that give them the satisfaction of a share in an important cooperative endeavor.[13]

Not only should there be sufficient business upon the agenda of board meetings, but the supervisors should be encouraged to make the decisions upon such problems. "Most people," the Region III office explains, "develop an interest in things they have to make a decision about." The experience of one board of supervisors in making decisions on priority of work was cited as a case in point:[14]

In one district where the governing body was not very active, this question was particularly troublesome to SCS technicians. When the problem was put up to the supervisors, they not only met their responsibilities toward it in fine shape, but went on to assume toward the whole program a much more active "directional role" than previously.

Thus, that Region urges district conservationists:

Encourage them [supervisors] to make all decisions on questions of policy and district administration.

How can that be done? One way is to *ask them* for their decision instead of making it for them. If Service personnel are asked by district supervisors (commissioners or directors) for recommendations,

---

[12] District Conservationists and Their Relationship with District Supervisors," *op. cit.,* p. 3.
[13] "District Conservationists Working with District Supervisors," prepared by States Relations Division, SCS, 1947.
[14] "Working with District Governing Bodies," *op. cit.,* pp. 1, 8.

they should give all the facts bearing on the question, suggest several alternative solutions, and leave the decision to the supervisors.

Reporting by technicians at board meetings on the progress and accomplishments of the districts also may leave supervisors with a sense of accomplishment. The Region V director suggests that district conservationists offer to present a report at each regular supervisors' meeting showing progress in planning farms and in the application of practices.[15] This practice is being increasingly followed in various sections of the country, district conservationists report.

Reports on district problems or progress in various activities are even more effective in arousing supervisor interest when they are made by supervisors themselves. In this manner supervisors are given a definite job to perform at each session. The reporting process of the Douglas County District, Washington, is described by the chairman of the board in a Washington state guide for supervisors:

At each meeting we have a report from our equipment supervisor, a progress report on farm planning and area problems, a report from our county agent on educational work as often as needed, and a report from one of our supervisors on cooperation with other groups, such as irrigation district, our livestock association, our county commissioners and our schools.

Some districts, such as the Pavillion District, Wyoming, have adopted the practice of sending out a summary of the accomplishments of the previous month along with the reminder of the next meeting.

Board meetings also have been found to be more satisfying when agendas are so arranged that the supervisors can move forward in an orderly fashion from one item of business to another. When supervisors with no prepared agenda flounder about in aimless discussion and do not isolate any particular problems for decision, they often leave meetings with a feeling of uselessness. As one midwestern supervisor expressed it: "Why go? We don't do anything." Supervisor handbooks or guides on district administration, issued by the state soil conservation committees, invariably urge district boards to adopt a regular order of business for board meetings, and usually suggest what that order of business might suitably be.

The preparation of an agenda also equips supervisors with an

---

[15] "District Conservationists and Their Relationship with District Supervisors," *op. cit.*, p. 3.

advance knowledge of problems to be considered. This knowledge gives them a sense of being able to contribute to the board's work. Merely sending out in advance a copy of the agenda for their meeting gives supervisors a chance to do a little thinking about the business to be handled at their meeting. Giving supervisors, in advance of meeting, written background material, and technicians talking individually with farmers about the problems on the agenda also increase supervisor willingness to make decisions in board meetings. In short, all of the devices which increase supervisor competence to make management decisions also tend to increase supervisor willingness to assume responsibility for making decisions.

The inadvisability of holding meetings when the board has little business to consider does not eliminate frequent, regularly scheduled meetings as an incentive to supervisor management of district affairs. As already pointed out, the boards which meet frequently and regularly, because they are in closer contact with the work of the district, have more decisions to reach at each meeting than do the boards which meet only infrequently.

DEVELOPING SUPERVISOR ESPRIT DE CORPS

The sense of *esprit de corps,* which so often impels men to work toward a common goal not directly identified with their immediate, narrow self-interests, is generally developed through two types of psychological supports: (1) the sense of being part of a large organized movement to which thousands of men scattered throughout the nation feel it is worth giving their energy; and (2) the sense of leadership prestige and responsibility that comes from local popular interest in and support of a community activity.

Sense of Leadership in a Community Undertaking

It is generally felt that if the district can grow into a strong community institution, supervisors will also develop a strong sense of leadership responsibility. As an Extension-SCS conservationist explains: "Public recognition of their position, their functions, and that they are performing a public service, is their due, and would act as a powerful stimulus to further activities on their part." The important thing, the Washington office observes, is to: ". . . encourage supervisors to see themselves as *serving the farmers* of the district (the district community) and primarily accountable to them rather than to the state body or others without the district."[16] In line with this thinking, the Georgia Extension conservationist wrote in a circular to district supervisors:

Who could be in a better position to serve his fellow man, both present and future, than a district soil conservation supervisor. Your friends selected you because (1) they know of your desire to serve; (2) they know your capabilities as a leader of your people; (3) they know you have the proper appreciation of the needs of people and their utter dependence upon our soil.

There are daily strategies in the routine operations of the district through which supervisors can be made conscious of their leadership in a genuine community undertaking. One of these strategies lies in the selection of the place for board meetings. Not only do board meetings in the local SCS office leave the supervisors with the feeling that conservation is an SCS show, but they further confuse rural people on the relationships of the Service to the district. The Service itself has been recommending that supervisor meetings should be held in places habitually used for community work, such as the courthouse, school, town hall, or church. Rotating the board's meeting place through various sections of the district frequently has been recommended as a means for creating farmer awareness of the district, and, consequently, for giving supervisors a feeling of their leadership responsibilities to farmers. Increasingly, supervisors in their annual reports mention rotating their meeting places.

Inviting farmers from the locality in which the supervisors are holding their session to sit in on the meeting is an extension of this device. The Region III office suggests that district boards might sometimes invite: ". . . local businessmen who own farms, the banker, the secretary of the Chamber of Commerce, etc., to meet with them. . . It not only gives outsiders an insight into the functioning of a district, but also develops leaders among the board members." [17] District board meetings, the Service admonishes, should not be packed with professional agricultural workers.

If supervisors are to appreciate that the district board is indeed the governing body of a local government, it is important that the officers of the district function in board meetings. Frequently even supervisors who have a sound, detailed understanding of conservation problems and the operations of the district are completely inexperienced in conducting a group meeting.

---

[16] "District Conservationists Working with District Supervisors," *op. cit.*
[17] "Working with District Governing Bodies," *op. cit.*, p. 6.

Board officers are prone to turn the meeting over to the professional workers.

The Service urges its technicians to work with officers in advance of each meeting, going over the problems which are to be brought up, and giving them tips on parliamentary procedures. District technicians, for their part, continually are being admonished by the higher administrative levels of the Service to withdraw from any leadership position in board meetings. The Washington office, for example, advises against technicians' bringing proposed courses of action directly to board meetings. It suggests that technicians talk over opportunities for board action with individual supervisors outside of the regular meeting and encourage them to make such suggestions to the board.

Basically, of course, supervisor sense of leadership prestige and responsibility in community conservation rests upon the degree to which the district is understood and supported by farmers as a unit of their local government. Thus, indirectly, all of the techniques for building up local popular support of conservation as a community activity will also instill in supervisors a sense of their leadership responsibilities.

Feeling of Participation in Large, Organized Movement

Supervisor awareness of being an integral part of a large, significant movement, which men throughout the country are finding worthy of their energies, is the second psychological basis for building supervisor *esprit de corps*. The state conservation committees, Extension conservationists, personnel of the Extension Services, and the staff of the Soil Conservation Service all have attempted to build up and foster within supervisors that sense of being a part of a dynamic, significant movement. But it has probably been the action of supervisors themselves in organizing their group into a cohesive independent association of district governing bodies which has been most useful in developing supervisor *esprit de corps*.

In all forty-eight states, district supervisors are now organized into state associations. During 1946 and early 1947, the "National Association of Soil Conservation District Governing Officials" was organized. The purpose of the association, as stated in its consitution, is ". . . to accelerate the effective functioning of soil conservation districts as democratically organized and operated local public instrumentalities."

The association does not list the creation of supervisor willingness actively to administer the affairs of the district as one of its means of achieving its large goal, but the spirit of the association is permeated with this drive. To quote a typical exhortation of the association's late president:

> In conclusion, may I state that, in my opinion, soil conservation district supervisors have the most important responsibility that any group of agricultural leaders have borne. . . . Supervisors, we have a job to do! Let us join hands in the great undertaking, realizing to the fullest extent our responsibility to our fellowman and to posterity.[18]

The carrying out of the specific purposes to which the association commits itself may also result in building supervisor *esprit de corps.* In the first place, the association according to its constitution is ". . . to facilitate the exchange of information, knowledge and experience among soil conservation districts; to collect, compile, and disseminate information relating to the organization and effective functioning of soil conservation districts." Although the inter-district dissemination of information to supervisors is primarily designed to increase supervisor competence in managing districts, it also aids in increasing supervisor willingness to perform district work. Secondly, the association proposes to use its organized force to secure greater material assistance for the districts:

> The Association intends to consult closely with officials of the United States Department of Agriculture — particularly the Secretary of Agriculture, the Soil Conservation Service and the Federal Office of Agricultural Extension, the members of — and the appropriate committees of — Congress, the national offices of farmer organizations, and allied interests. The Association will encourage and assist the state organizations of soil conservation districts, and the districts themselves, to help officials of the Federal Government, state government and private organizations and individuals to become acquainted and keep conversant with the work of the soil conservation districts in their home territories.[19]

As supervisors in their organized group grow as a force in national and state agricultural politics, their cohesive spirit of group independence and strength also grows. In an attempt to appraise the effect that the organization of supervisors into their own association has had upon supervisor administration, the

---

[18] E. C. McArthur, "Opportunities and Possibilities in Solving Soil Conservation and Land-Use Problems Through Districts," address before Fourth Annual Conference of Louisiana Soil Conservation District Supervisors, Baton Rouge, November 12, 1942, p. 5.

[19] "Plan of Action for National Association of Soil Conservation Districts," prepared and revised by the late President of the Association, E. C. McArthur, after correspondence and consultation with the Directors, May 5, 1947, p. 2.

observations of the Florida state conservationist might be taken as summing up the typical effect in all states:

The most outstanding activity that has influenced district administration was the organization of the Florida Association of Soil Conservation District Supervisors in May of 1946. This organization has already proven itself to be a going concern and the influence and stimulation it has provided for individual districts has been like magic. Almost overnight individual supervisors and district boards became aggressive and determined. The organization has seemed to enable supervisors generally to visualize the district movement as it should be and realize their responsibility for making it click.

In general the vehicles which the supervisors' associations, state committees, and the staffs of federal and state agricultural agencies have used also make for supervisor *esprit de corps*. These media are: group meetings of supervisors on an area, state, or national basis, news bulletins, circular letters and other publications, personal discussions and correspondence.

Bringing together supervisors on an area, state, or national basis, for one, two, or three day get togethers has been primarily for the purpose of educating supervisors in their management tasks. Yet the by-product of these meetings — supervisor *esprit de corps* — has sometimes been equally important in strengthening supervisor administration.

Within a state, the state association, state committee, Extension conservationist, and the staffs of SCS and the Extension Service usually work together as a team in arranging for area or state supervisor meetings. Thirty-three state conservation committees, according to the replies of forty-three states to the writer's questionnaire,[20] arrange for joint meetings of district governing bodies. Generally the state supervisors association works closely with the state committee in organizing the meetings. In California, Colorado, Montana, and South Dakota, where the state committees are not reported as organizing joint meetings, the Extension conservationists explain that this function is left to the supervisor associations.

Bringing supervisors together through printed media also is being used increasingly to stir supervisor enthusiasm for their district work. Nineteen state committees, of the forty-three reporting states, are now preparing and sending circular letters to district supervisors. In California, Minnesota, and Mississippi

---

[20] Five states—Arkansas, Kentucky, Oklahoma, South Carolina, and Tennessee—did not reply to questionnaire. See Appendix B.

the supervisors associations perform this function. The state committee sometimes has its own executive secretary who is responsible for this editorial work, but frequently it is the Extension conservationist who prepares such circulars in the name of the state committee. Sometimes, as in Idaho, circulars on district activities go out under the name of the Extension conservationist. In Massachusetts, the Extension Service, acting for the state committee, publishes a periodical. Frequently the state associations circularize the experiences of individual districts.

Such circulars usually take the form of newsletters. They are largely in the nature of exhortations, and are usually composed of the experiences, problems, and progress of the various districts within the state. Even the titles of these circular publications are suggestive of their exhortatory character. In New York, the newsletter is called, *Down to Earth;* in Maryland, *On the Level;* in Georgia, *Saving Georgia Soils through Districts;* in Michigan, *News and Views.* Sometimes excerpts from the minutes of district boards are prepared and distributed, either separately or incorporated in the more general newsletter. In twenty-eight of the forty-three reporting states, the state committees receive copies of the minutes of the meetings of district governing bodies. Twenty-one of forty-three state committees whose activities were reported have had summaries or excerpts of district annual reports prepared and distributed to district supervisors.

The third general medium for bringing supervisors out of the isolation of their district into the general district conservation movement is supervisors' personal contacts with the leaders in their state associations, the members of the state committee or the committee's staff, and with the Extension conservationists.

A third of the states now are paying at least part of the salary of a committee executive secretary or field representative, whose job is to spend a large share of his time working with supervisors in their districts. A few state committees also employ additional staff. For example, the Wisconsin state committee employs erosion control men as field representatives. A supervisory mechanic is employed by the West Virginia state committee.

Committee members themselves often make it a practice to meet regularly with the supervisors. Sometimes a state is divided into areas, and each committee member is made responsible for visiting the district boards in his area. Personal contact with district governing bodies is perhaps the most important single function of the Extension conservationist in each state. In addition, the leaders of the state supervisors association movement usually are alert to their responsibility for personally exhorting supervisors to greater efforts.

EDUCATING SUPERVISORS FOR DISTRICT ADMINISTRATION

However interested in community conservation and however anxious to help with district work supervisors may be, successful supervisor administration of a district will not develop unless supervisors are trained for district management. They must have considerable understanding of the conservation problems of the lands of the district and of the technical measures for preventing erosion and restoring soil fertility. They must have a clear perception of the nature of the district device and of their duties and responsibilities in managing the district. Finally, they must understand the operational problems of the district and the administrative arrangements and techniques suitable for carrying out community conservation.

Knowledge of Conservation Problems and Control Measures

Perhaps the single most important need in supervisor administration is farmer supervisor education in the physical problems of conservation and in erosion control treatments. The soundness of supervisors' decisions as administrators depends upon how well they understand the purpose, mechanics, and interrelationships of such erosion control measures as farming on the contour, strip cropping, terracing, providing grassed waterways through fields, constructing soil-saving dams, turning steep slopes to timber production, shelterbelt planting, etc. Supervisors usually are selected from those farmers who have led the movement to organize a district. But often the supervisors, at the founding of the district, have not yet begun to apply combined conservation treatment to their own farms. Over and over the need for supervisor education in the physical tasks of conservation is stressed. A committee of professional workers in the Pacific Coast Region declared:

Governing bodies usually do not recognize and understand the district's basic resources, the problems and their solutions, and until they do, they cannot be entirely successful in running the district.[21]

The Montana state soil conservation committee explained:

---

[21] "Speeding up Production," report of a special SCS committee, Region VII, p. 2.

Successful district administration depends to a large extent upon the district supervisors' knowledge of the problems to be met and the work to be done as set forth in the district program and work plans. To secure satisfactory administration, supervisors must be willing to give some time to studying conservation needs.[22]

All of the vehicles for stimulating supervisor interest in district work also have been used to educate them in the technical problems of conservation. The primary means of increasing supervisor understanding are the daily routine contacts between Service technicians and supervisors. The Service constantly urges its field workers to increase supervisor understanding in the technical phases of conservation. During the meetings of the board, the technician is to be constantly alert to giving supervisors an accurate, detailed picture of the conservation problems on the various lands in the district. Through his systematically reporting on the problems he has encountered and the technical progress he has been making, the technician has an opportunity to build up supervisor understanding.

Technicians talking over with individual supervisors, outside of their regular meetings, specific conservation problems or treatments, has been emphasized as a particularly effective educational technique. The Region III office explains:

> In addition to presenting soil conservation material in meetings of district governing bodies, much good work can be done by the district conservationist in his day-to-day personal contacts with the individual members of the board.[23]

The example of a supervisor who, having a lot of tile-drained land on his farm, was considered somewhat of an authority on tile drains by farmers in the district, was cited to illustrate the dangers of supervisor misinformation and the potentialities for the district program in educating supervisors through personal discussion. The memorandum continues:

> . . . from time to time he has given farmers information on tile outlets that is not in line with technical recommendations. Here is a case where personal work in the field with this man might result in directing his influence into channels that would promote a sound drainage program in the district, instead of resulting in the confusion of conflicting information as between the supervisor and the technician.

Taking supervisors either singly or as a group to areas where

---

[22] "Suggestions Regarding Soil Conservation District Administration," prepared by the Montana State Soil Conservation Committee, December 14, 1945, p. 1.
[23] "Working with District Governing Bodies," *op. cit.,* p. 4.

particular types of conservation problems are being met makes such problems more concrete and real to supervisors. In Minnesota, the practice has been established of taking supervisors on a tour of their district before either the district program or work plan is written. The tour includes the problem areas in the district. Accompanying the supervisors are the county agent, district conservationist, and soils specialist from the college. A soils map is prepared by the SCS soils man before the tour, and soil profiles are studied during the course of the tour. Frequently such supervisor tours are extended into neighboring districts in order that supervisors in the newly created district may see conservation problems in the process of being worked out on the ground. For example, in Oregon, the Sauvie Island, Southern Wasco, and Langell Valley Districts have held a number of tours for supervisors from other districts. In the area meetings of Utah supervisors, it is reported that:

> The idea of a correlation program to acquaint each district with practices being carried on in other districts received definite approval at all meetings and some good suggestions were made by discussion leaders to include tours to other districts and when possible to other states.[24]

Probably the most effective method of developing supervisor understanding of conservation problems is through a sort of inservice training program, in which supervisors take part in the actual development of farm plans and help in the initiation of various types of practices. This is in addition to carrying out the management work of the district which also builds up an insight into district conservation problems.

Another means district professional workers have for educating supervisors in the physical problems of conservation is the preparation of brief informational statements upon conservation problems and undertakings within the district. Explains the Region III office:

> Another means of giving the governing body soil conservation information that is effectively employed is to place in the hands of each supervisor short, concise statements covering the more important practices and measures set up in the program and work plan of the district. These sheets serve as reference material to the supervisors after the practices have been discussed in the meetings of the governing body. The possession of this information gives these men a feel-

---

[24] "Report on Five Area Meetings," *op. cit.*, p. 3.

ing of confidence in their discussions of soil conservation practices with farmers throughout the district.[25]

The state committees, usually working with the Extension conservationist, the staffs of the Extension Service, or the state SCS office, also have undertaken to present informational material upon conservation problems and practices. Twenty-nine of the forty-three reported state committees are characterized as working with technical and educational agencies to provide literature helpful to individual district programs. Fourteen state committees were reported as collaborating with other state agencies in providing the districts with technical guides.[26]

Bringing specialists from the state colleges into board meetings is another device sometimes employed for acquainting supervisors with the variety of land use and related agricultural problems which affect the accomplishment of conservation. To give a typical case: A specialist from the state college attended the board meeting of the Mills County District, Iowa, to explain to supervisors the landlord and tenant relationship in establishing and paying for soil conservation practices.

The programs of the area and state meetings of district supervisors are always designed to give supervisors better understanding of conservation problems and erosion control measures. Supervisor meetings on the area basis have been found to be particularly well adapted for educating supervisors in the technical problems of conservation. In Utah, district supervisors, after their experience in meeting together on an area basis, agreed that:

> The annual area meetings, such as were held this year, had advantages over a state-wide meeting in that they provided more opportunity for discussion of local problems, but that every other year a state-wide meeting should be held to discuss problems of a completely state-wide nature, which could not be handled in district type or area meetings. [27]

Realization of Governing Responsibilities

Equally important in building active supervisor administration is giving governing boards a clear perspective of the nature of the district device, its strategic role in community conservation, and of supervisor management responsibilities in the district program. Supervisors generally do not yet have a sufficiently clear perception of the district and their own responsibilities under

[25] "Working with District Governing Bodies," *op. cit.,* pp. 5, 6.
[26] *See* Appendix B.
[27] "Report on Five Area Meetings," *op. cit.,* p. 6.

state law. Frequently supervisors look upon the conservation program as belonging to SCS or the county agent. Like farmers generally, they quite often refer to the district as the "Soil Conservation *Service* District." As in their relationships with the county agent, supervisors are prone to look to the technicians to run the program and to speak in terms of "helping out the boys." So confused as to the nature of the district-agency relationships was one supervisor interviewed that he spoke of the county agent as the work unit conservationist's "boss." Sometimes supervisors are not even clear as to whether they were elected or appointed.

District supervisors, as well as the professional agricultural workers, generally realize the need for a careful educational program for informing supervisors of their duties, responsibilities, and authority. Without such understanding as a basis for action, district governing bodies cannot proceed with confidence. A supervisor in a Utah district expressed this need in telling terms:

> We supervisors need a better understanding of our job. If a man is ambitious and energetic, he does not want someone else doing the work he was elected to do. Every so often something comes up that should be done and we are told it was our job to have done it. It is probably the first time that we have ever heard of it. We supervisors cannot perform our duties if we do not know what they are.

The viewpoint of the professional field worker on educating supervisors in their legal responsibilities was well expressed by a district conservationist in the South. "The problem of convincing supervisors that they must be more than rubber stamps is largely a matter of acquainting supervisors with their responsibilities." In a similar vein, the Region III office suggests:

> With all new governing bodies and periodically with old ones arrange for a review and discussion of the state districts law, particularly with regard to their responsibilities. . . . Merely reading the state districts law aloud and discussing parts of it will usually get the results.[28]

Although district conservationists are in a position to explain to supervisors their duties and responsibilities, it is generally agreed that supervisor education is more effective when administered by the districts' own state committee than by the representative of a federal agency. Thirty-six out of forty-three state committees now provide their districts with some sort of literature explaining state laws.[29] It is increasingly becoming the

---

[28] "Working with District Governing Bodies," *op. cit.*, p. 1.
[29] *See* Appendix B.

practice for members of the state committee, or its executive secretary or field representative, to lead discussions of the state laws with each of the district boards. In Texas, for example, a representative of the state board, usually accompanied by the Extension conservationist, meets with the supervisors to install them in office. At that time, information is given to the supervisors as to their functions, how supervisors work in other districts, and the kinds of opportunities they are finding for contributing in a significant way to the advancement of soil conservation. One of the first responsibilities of the state Extension conservationist is to give governing bodies an adequate understanding of the district, and of their responsibilities, opportunities, and capacities for managing their district programs. District supervisors' responsibilities are, of course, invariably emphasized in their own association meetings.

Understanding of Practical Workings of District

Supervisors need a clear, detailed understanding of the operational and housekeeping problems involved in the district's getting conservation measures applied upon farmers' lands. First, supervisors must appreciate what the district's operating problems are; what the major conservation emphasis of the district should be; what activities or programs might be undertaken by the district; what the relationships between farmer cooperator and district should properly be; how equipment is to be secured, operated, and maintained; the extent to which the district should undertake to obtain conservation materiel; and so on. Secondly, supervisors must understand the various courses of action, arrangements or procedures open to the district in each of these problem areas. They must be equipped with all the facts for making decisions. Not only must supervisors understand the operating or action problems of the district, but they need guidance and assistance in carrying on the housekeeping functions in district administration — that is, the handling of records, preparing of reports, keeping of financial accounts, performing of audits, and so on.

It is in this wide area of supervisor education that professional workers have their opportunity for developing active, competent supervisor administration. Since 1944, with the Service itself as the driving force, the state committees, supervisors associations, Extension conservationists, and staffs of Extension Service and SCS have been devoting increasing attention to giving supervisors that sort of positive education and training

Fig. 14 — A severely gullied area in Georgia.

Fig. 15 — Area shown in Fig. 14 three years after planting kudzu.

in the administrative workings of the district, which actually equip supervisors to take over the management of the various activities in district administration.

Twenty-five of the forty-three reported state committees are now providing supervisors with a handbook or manual on the organizations, procedures, and working processes of district administration. The handbooks provide supervisors with such general information as explanations of the purpose of the district, powers and duties of supervisors, laws and legal opinions relative to district operations, sources of assistance, and relationships with the state committee and the assisting federal and state agencies. They also usually outline in a one-two-three fashion the steps to be taken by governing bodies in getting a district into operation: organizing the board, preparing district program and work plan, requesting educational and operating assistance from federal and state agencies, and the like.

Since the state committees usually have special responsibilities in district housekeeping activities, the manuals frequently give considerable attention to such particulars as rules for keeping minutes of official proceedings, establishing systems for proper handling of funds, accounting and auditing of finances, the carrying of insurance, and the need for surety bonds. Frequently, sample methods or forms for keeping such records are provided.

Quite generally the manuals give at least brief explanations of such operational problems as the carrying on of educational programs, determining priority of work areas, importance of the farm conservation plan, use of farmer-district agreements, and the acquisition, operation, maintenance and repair of equipment. Increasingly, the manuals are attempting to give supervisors a background of facts to be considered in making operating decisions. For example, the Illinois handbook explains to supervisors:

Before acquiring equipment of any type, the directors should consider three questions:

(1) Is the equipment really needed? Oftentimes available machinery can be made to do the job.

(2) Is such equipment available from any other source? Contractors will frequently do work requiring special machinery at reasonable cost if sufficient work is lined up to prevent delays in operation and long, expensive moves.

(3) Will the probable rental charge provide for depreciation and upkeep, as well as costs of routing and collecting fees for use of equipment?

Generally, however, the manuals do not equip supervisors with sufficiently detailed background information and pertinent factors for making their variety of operating decisions.

The supervisors associations and the Extension conservationists have been particularly effective in supplementing the handbooks with more concrete, detailed, and current information for carrying on the operational activities of the district. A series of panel discussions in which supervisors exchange their experiences in particular district problems is usually featured in supervisor meetings. To illustrate, in their 1951 state association meeting, Iowa commissioners held a panel discussion on the impact of Secretary Brannan's Memorandum 1278 upon the role of district commissioners. In five area meetings in Utah, supervisors led discussions on the following problems:

> . . . proper organization of district boards; by-laws and election policies; development of annual and long-time district programs; what the educational program for districts should consist of; methods of acquainting each district with practices being carried on in other districts; minutes, reports, accounting systems, and audits; operation and management of heavy equipment; the advantageous use of Federal, State, and county organizations in the program of soil conservation.[30]

The Extension conservationists are in a peculiarly advantageous position for currently informing district supervisors on successful methods and procedures developed in various districts, on how supervisors in other districts are tackling particular problems, and so on. Through their work with supervisors, their close contacts with Service personnel in the districts, and through their perusal of district reports and minutes of governing bodies, they are in a strategic position for gleaning new ideas on supervisor administration. Again, through their personal contacts with supervisors and district Service personnel and through the medium of newsletters, they can pass these tips along to other supervisors.

ORGANIZING DISTRICT ADMINISTRATION TO
FACILITATE SUPERVISOR MANAGEMENT

Effective supervisor administration of conservation activity cannot be expected to result solely from supervisors' willingness to serve in district work and from their trained competence. District administration itself must be so organized that it can be ade-

---

[30] Letter from Ivan L. Hobson and J. L. Boatman, to all Extension Conservationists, May 20, 1947, p. 8.

quately carried on by a group of reasonably well-equipped lay citizens. The work of the district must be in a manageable form in all its administrative dimensions — volume of work, area of work, and timing of work.

Division of Administrative Work of District

The breaking down of the total administrative work of the district into smaller tasks of manageable size, and then isolating the responsibility for carrying out each task in one or two of the supervisors, is in accordance with a well-proved principle of effective administration. The Service has seen the organizing of supervisor activity around such breakdowns in the district administrative load as one of the most important factors in the obtaining of a real supervisor administration. Breakdowns in district administration may be made both on functional and area bases.

FUNCTIONAL SPECIALIZATION OF ACTIVITY

The most common functional specialization is in the assignment of equipment responsibilities — collecting rentals, routing equipment, overseeing its maintenance and repair. The Service has insisted upon such isolation of equipment responsibilities as essential to an adequate equipment usage plan. Another usual specialization of work is the grouping of jobs generally performed by a secretary-treasurer of any organized group activity — the keeping of financial records and accounts, minutes of meetings, and so on. Quite commonly, the secretary-treasurer of the district board, because the largest amount of district record keeping involves the operation of equipment, is also made equipment supervisor.

Frequently, governing bodies have organized either temporary or standing committees of two or three supervisors for such tasks as the purchasing, selling, and distribution of conservation materiel, for conservation education in the district, for long-range plans for conservation work, for a forestry program, and for preparation of the annual report or annual work plan. For example, in the Hardy County District, West Virginia, two members of the board were made responsible for the operation of the district's lime plant.

The practice of specializing responsibility according to problems has not as yet, however, become general. When such assignments are made, they are usually on an informal basis. The description by a supervisor of a Tennessee district of the odd jobs he does for the district is quite typical. He speaks of being asked by the secretary of the board to speak to the Lions Club, and later of being chosen to represent the district at a meeting of middle Tennessee supervisors. Too frequently, the only specialization that occurs in district board administration is leaving the chairman with the heft of the district jobs.

Territorial Division of Administrative Work

Dividing district management work into geographical areas is much more customary than functional breakdowns. This territorial division of responsibility has been strongly advised by the Service, state committees, and Extension conservationists. Almost all committee handbooks urge district boards to divide their responsibilities into supervisorial areas. The advice in the handbook of the Washington state committee nicely summarizes this arrangement:

In preparing for active operations most district governing bodies find it desirable to divide their district into supervisorial areas and to give the supervisor residing therein authority to perform certain duties and functions of the governing body in which the concurrence of other members is not required. These duties and responsibilities consist of such things as securing applications for farm plans, the routing of equipment within their area, holding local meetings either to arrange for an operation program or for educational purposes, securing receipts from cooperators for materials made available to them, assisting cooperators in their community in the establishment and carrying out of conservation measures and others of like character.

It is only the exceptional district board which has not thus divided, either formally or informally, at least some of its responsibilities. The two most frequent responsibilities assumed by each supervisor in his own area has been the reviewing and approval of farm plans and the management of equipment when it is operating in his zone. This equipment management usually consists of the supervisor's deciding who will use the equipment at certain times and making necessary financial arrangements. Frequently, light equipment is stored on his own farm, and farmer cooperators get it from him and return it to him. Sometimes the division of work into supervisorial areas has been characterized as mere paper assignments. But it can generally be discovered that the boards whose supervisors individually are not performing the work of the district in their own areas are not, as a group, adequately carrying their total management responsibilities.

Problem of Area in District Administration

The territorial division of the district into areas of individual supervisor responsibility in part succeeds in breaking down the total administrative load of a district board into manageable areas of operation. But it does not overcome the obstacles that over-large districts set up against active supervisor administration. Particularly in the early days of the developing district program, the Soil Conservation Service strongly urged the organization of districts upon the basis of watersheds or other natural erosion areas. Often the resulting districts were of considerable size, comprising several counties.[31]

Experience in the operation of these large districts has revealed them ill-proportioned for supervisor administration. First, the very size of the district creates a time-distance obstacle to supervisors' actively carrying their management responsibilities. The supervisors of the Tallahatchie River District, Mississippi, which covers nearly a million acres, have been so keenly aware of the distance factor's impairing their effective functioning that they have stressed it through a series of annual reports. In 1940, they explained:

With the Commissioners [Supervisors] located in various parts of the District, it is necessary for them to travel a great distance in order to get together for a meeting when there is business to be transacted. . . . This fact usually results in the affairs of the district going unattended.

Again, in 1942, they raised the same problem:

Considering the fact that the average round trip travel distance for each Commissioner is fifty-four miles, the presence of a quorum at each meeting is a good indication of the interest of the Board of Commissioners in the work of the District. Necessarily, an increasing amount of the District business is carried on through the medium of the District Conservationist, who serves as an intermediary in exchanging ideas of the Commissioners, and obtaining their thought and attention on various problems which come up periodically, yet do not justify a called meeting of the Commission.

In 1945, they reported:

In order to help us out due to our inability to get together more often, we have relied on the District Conservationist to keep us informed of District-wide problems.

---

[31] For current compilations of number, size and location of all districts, see "Soil Conservation Districts: Status of Organization, Approximate Acreage, Number of Operating Units and Farms in Organized Districts." This information is processed and distributed semi-annually by the Soil Conservation Service.

The same story is repeated once again in 1946:

Only three meetings were held during the year. Since considerable travel is involved on the part of Commissioners to attend a meeting, the number of meetings have been purposely held to the minimum. Most of the business has been handled through committees.

Secondly, one of the chief merits of local conservation government — farmer supervisors' knowledge of the district's special local conditions and their understanding of the opinions and reactions of farmers in the district — is in danger of being lost in large districts. As a district conservationist in the South explains: "Farmers usually are unable to see even county-wide. They know very little about other communities in their county, and know next to nothing about conditions in other counties." The hesitancy of supervisors to pass judgment on conservation plans because they do not know the farms, reveals how lack of local knowledge impairs supervisor activity.

Finally, another advantage of local government is lost if the district is so large that its government is not easily accessible to its farmers. The Region IV director early pointed out this advantage of small districts after a few months of working with both large and small districts:

If we passed our judgment on what has happened in the last ten months, we should say the Districts should be small, because the smaller districts in Arkansas where the supervisors know each other and their people know them, where the county agent and vocational agriculture teachers knew everyone, they have really gone to town. In a big district, the personnel may have been in there ten months, but it is hard to find them.[32]

In some large districts, governing boards have attempted to make themselves more accessible by rotating their meetings through various sections of the districts.

The setting up of small districts may not permit conservation activity to enjoy the technical advantages arising out of organization on a larger watershed basis. The creation of small districts perhaps adds even further to the confusion of local governments by sheer force of extra numbers. Finally, as the Region IV director pointed out, the creation of many small districts may develop for federal and state assisting agencies an administrative problem which would be so top-heavy that it would overbalance all other

---

[32] Louis P. Merrill, "Policies of the Administration of Region 4 in Assisting Oklahoma Soil Conservation Districts," address in "Short Course, Oklahoma Soil Conservation Districts," Stillwater, February 1, 2, 1939, p. 37.

considerations.[33] Yet in all, if the district device is in essence an effort to bring local government into public conservation activity, the advantages of the small district probably outweigh its demerits.

Timing Dimension in Supervisor Administration

The timing dimension in supervisor administration is also a critical factor in determining the degree of supervisor formulation and control of district policies. Supervisors must have opportunities, in terms of time, to equip themselves for making the decisions for which they are to take the responsibility. The time factor in supervisor administration involves two measurements of time. The first is in terms of the stage of district development or operation; the second, in terms of any specific problem or activity the supervisors are considering or undertaking.

Perhaps the greatest incongruity in the Department of Agriculture's drive for the local determination of conservation policies has been its requirement that the newly created district, through its inexperienced supervisors, formally set down the working policies of the district and commit itself to them in a work plan. The Service always has stressed that these documents (district program and work plan) should reflect the thinking of local people and should vary in whatever respects are required to best meet the local needs. Yet, however strongly the Service urges supervisors and their assisting farmer committees to use their own experience and judgments in formulating their work plans, however energetically district technicians attempt to equip supervisors with background information, however sincerely professional workers try to withdraw from leadership in program and work plan development, it is likely that district policies, when drawn up in this early stage in the district's life, will be largely the thinking of the professional agricultural workers.

That the work plan's preparation at the very beginning of district operations was no machination on the part of the Service to control district policies was shown by SCS's attempting, through its field technicians, to goad supervisors into periodic revisions of their original work plan. The work plan was looked upon by the Service as:

. . . a continuing, progressively improved and revised, workable plan of district action, to be kept current as more information becomes available, new types of work are to be done, new methods of doing the

---
[33] *Ibid.*, p. 39.

same work become known or available, or certain problems demand particular courses of action not previously contemplated.[34]

Such revisions by district supervisors came only slowly and painfully, however. Therefore, the Service turned to the idea of the annual plan of work.

The primary motive of the Service in urging the district to adopt an annual plan of operation and calendar of activities was probably to provide cooperating agencies and farm groups with a single official source of unified current direction for the administration of district affairs. But the deciding of policies annually, after operatng experience has been accumulated by the supervisors, also serves to remove any obstacles to supervisor determination of district policies which the Service's insistence upon an original work plan may have set up.

Supervisors, through the annual plan of work, have a real opportunity to redetermine their operating policies. This is revealed by the Region II suggestions on what should be included in such a plan:

A. What proportion of the job ahead as shown in the Program will be set as a goal for this year?

B. How many farms should be planned?

C. What amounts of each practice or what percentage of the estimated quantities of practices should be applied with equipment and facilities available at present time?

D. What efforts will the Governing Body make to secure additional needed equipment and materials?

E. Where will work be concentrated this year?

F. What does the Governing Body propose to do this year in the way of an Educational Program? Number and kinds of meetings? Sources of assistance?

G. What community projects will be undertaken this year and how much of each? Drainage? Highway erosion control? Stream bank and channel improvement?[35]

Through the promptings of the Service's field staff, state committees, and Extension conservationists, the districts are steadily turning to the annual preparation of work plans. In several states, all of the districts are now developing annual plans. For example, the Nebraska state conservationist reports:

The developement of annual work plans is accepted as a matter of

---

[34] F. S. Fisher, Projects Plans Division, SCS Region III, "Programs and Work Plans of Farmers' (Not Our) Soil Conservation Districts," an address at SCS regional conference, December 1942, p. 5.

[35] "Annual Plan of Operation," prepared by SCS Region II, March 20, 1947, p. 2.

course by the supervisors and a great deal of constructive thought and direction have been put into these by supervisors throughout the state.

District supervisors at the beginning of a district's operation are no more equipped to set up long term objectives for their district than they are to outline its working processes. Because of this, the Service staff in North Dakota also has been seeking a procedure for getting around the departmental requirement that a district must develop a suitable program before the Department can enter into a memorandum of understanding with it. The device being experimented with is a preliminary program, in which supervisors simply point out in very large terms the conservation problems of the district with the understanding that a more comprehensive program will be worked out later. Several of these preliminary programs of North Dakota districts now have been accepted as a basis for departmental cooperation. Thus, supervisors in North Dakota have been given an opportunity to learn the work of the district before determining its goals.

The second type of time opportunity which supervisors require for competent determination of district policies is intervals of time in which to study any specific problem facing the board. Such time intervals are particularly necessary if supervisors are to contribute at all to the formulation of their original work program and work plan. Expecting inexperienced farmer supervisors to make any real contribution to formulating district policies when they are called together to prepare their policy documents during the course of a single day is completely unrealistic. More suitable is the procedure, now quite frequently followed, of devoting several meetings to its preparation. In the interim periods supervisors and their assisting committees work through information given them or prepare specific parts of the program or work plan. The preparation of the Towaliga District, Georgia, program and work plan, as explained in that document, typifies this procedure:

The supervisors developed this Program of the District in several meetings and over a period of several weeks. In the beginning of the preparation of the Program and Plan of Work, outlines for each were adopted and sections of the outline were given to each supervisor to prepare, with the assistance of the County Agent, other technical workers, and farmer groups before the next meeting. At the next meeting of the supervisors, each supervisor from the county would read the sections as prepared in the county by that supervisor and those assisting him since the previous meeting. There would be a full discussion of each section and such changes and amendments as agreed on by the whole group would be made. When all sections had been adopted by sections, typed copies of the entire document were supplied to each supervisor for study prior to the meeting for adoption.

This same type of timing sequence is desirable in all stages of district operations. The Service urges its field workers to aid boards in organizing their work so that a list of the problems to be considered may be prepared and distributed to supervisors in advance of their meeting day. Supplying background information on the problems to be considered in board meetings is also a part of the timing technique.

In all the efforts to strengthen supervisor administration— the creating of administrative arrangements facilitating supervisor management, the developing of and employing of incentive techniques and devices, the educating and training of supervisors in the problems and workings of local conservation adminis- tration — the Service generally has taken the initiative. It has been SCS which has stimulated state committees and Extension conser- vationists in their work to develop supervisor management. More- over, the Service has increasingly insisted that its own field per- sonnel render assistance in such a way that district governing bodies will assume their rightful responsibilities.[36]

A former district conservationist of an Illinois district re- counts how, after having had a wonderful time running the governing body for the first two years, he was forced by SCS, despite the objections of the supervisors, to refuse to carry on the management work of the supervisors.

Despite the insistence of top SCS administrative levels that Service technicians refuse to do the work of the supervisors, it has been exceedingly difficult for the technicians thus to dis- engage themselves. As the Illinois district conservationist ex- plained, "It was easier to do the work myself than try to get them to do it." Moreover, the professional workers, quite humanly, have a tendency to feel that they know better what is suitable for the district than do the supervisors. They grow impatient with their supervisors' relative incompetency in technical matters and their delays in management work.

Finally, as employees of the Soil Conservation Service, they feel that their professional careers are dependent upon making a showing through their districts' conservation accomplishments. The reluctance of technicians to shift district work to the super-

---

[36] F. S. Fisher, *op. cit.,* p. 2.

visors is often due to their feeling of administrative responsibility, in the SCS hierarchy, for the successful functioning of their districts. This is shown by the success the Service has had in forcing supervisors to write their own annual reports. By absolutely forbidding its technicians to prepare such reports and absolving them from all responsibility for them, the Service has largely separated its field workers from this task. Nevertheless, the local technician's greatest problem in shifting the management work to the supervisors is supervisor reluctance to accept such duties and responsibilities. In short, the development of Service-district functional interdependence has not been a matter of SCS wresting power from local people. Rather, the Service is continually attempting to goad local people into participating in the district process.

The fact still remains, however, that the Service, in its effort to establish national soil conservation, feels that it must give the two thousand-odd local districts a necessary minimum of operational guidance. Although the Service may, through its authorizing agreements with the districts, set up certain minimum administrative policies to which the districts must adhere on penalty of losing Service assistance, SCS has not seen it as expedient thus to guide or control district activities. Rather, it has been depending increasingly upon its field staff so to advise district boards that their administrations ". . . agree fundamentally with the policies of the assisting Service." [37]

The large question in Service-district relationships still remains, then, for the future to answer. Can there be developed a suitable constructive balancing of Service-district relationships? If supervisor government does indeed strengthen as a result of the Service's program to activate district boards, will these boards be so convinced of the rightness of technician advice that they will be content to adhere to Service policies?

---

[37] "Guiding Principles and Policies," *op. cit.* p. cont'd.

CHAPTER 6

Value of District in
Achieving Soil Conservation

The value of the soil conservation district in achieving nation-wide conservation coverage has been fundamentally challenged on two chief bases. The first questioning of the district program's value rises from the premise that erosion and depletion of soil fertility are only symptoms of what Charles Kellogg, Chief of the Division of Soil Survey, describes as deep maladjustments between the soil and the farming system.[1]

The basic obstacles to conservation are rooted deep in the political, economic, social, and institutional structure. Unsuitable tenure relationships, uneconomic size farms, lack of adequate credit, inappropriate taxation formulas, unstable economic conditions, absence of needed skills — all are formidable obstacles to the achievement of conservation. Consequently, so the argument runs, no simple direct program concentrating on physical conservation measures alone can carry through the complete national conservation job.

After conservation practices have been established on the lands of those farmers whose institutional arrangements are best suited to undertaking conservation, the district, if it retains its present simple program, will find it increasingly difficult to get conservation measures carried out on the remaining untreated acres. The need, then, is for developing a total agricultural program made up of a series of integrated agricultural and rural life activities which will facilitate the physical conservation program.

The desirability of such a total remedial agricultural program need not be spelled out. But the possibility of such a program's

---

[1] For a summary and explanation of this position see Charles M. Hardin, "Land or People?", *Land Economics*, Vol. XVII, May, 1951, pp. 133–142.

materializing in the foreseeable future is slight. In the first place, the area of present public responsibility and authority is too limited to permit governmental elimination of the institutional obstacles to conservaton. Charles Hardin, in his advocacy of an alternative goal to physical soil conservation — the improvement of farm family living on a soil-conserving base — is quick to point out the obstacles to the achievement of such a program.

It seems necessary to stress the elemental point that this kind of public action is outside the ability of any combination of administrative agencies. . . . If improvement of farm family living seems to call for new lines of credit and tenure reform, for example, no possible combination of public agencies, however effectively cooperating, would be enough to carry it through. So long as a major fraction of agricultural credit is handled by private individuals and banks, the provision of credit for farm enlargements and improvements will need to be developed through some kind of agreement with private lenders.[2]

Not only is the area of public authority limited, but the American federal system leaves so much of this authority with the states that the national government's potential for action is even further reduced. For example, state law controls the system of real property taxation, tenure relationships, and land-use regulation. Finally, no really suitable blueprint has yet been developed for gearing together into an harmonious program the variety of activities of the federal government in agriculture, and for integrating them with the programs of the state agricultural agencies. Nor is it likely that either political or bureaucratic pressures would permit such a rationalized administration soon to develop.

The value of the district in achieving conservation cannot be written off because it fails to measure up to an ideal model of programming, which seemingly is impossible of achievement under the present limited area of government, the federal system, and existing political and bureaucratic pressures. Rather, the task is to appraise the district in terms of what kind of optimum program is possible within the present institutional framework. Still, within these limitations, the district will have the task of demonstrating that it can meet future conservation needs, at least as well as any other agency or combination of agencies, and that it has the potential for being geared into the broader conservation program the future may require.

The second line of question concerning the value of the

---

[2] *Ibid.*, p. 141.

district in carrying on conservation also is in the nature of a comparison to an ideal model. But this model, rather than being institutional in character, is the quantitative economic model of efficiency in the use of resources in conservation. It raises the question of whether the district is making the most economical use possible of the resources society wishes devoted to conservation.[3]

Conservation, according to an analysis by Earl Heady, is the prevention of the "diminution of output in the future from given resource inputs." Efficiency in the use' of limited public conservation funds is "denoted by allocations which minimize the potential diminution of future production when given resources are applied to the land." According to this guide-line of efficiency in the use of resources for conservation, the following principles are to be observed in determining conservation activity.

First, resources assigned to conservation should be used only for true conservation practices. For example, irrigation, drainage, and weed control are not practices which are generally necessary to prevent a decrease in future production. Green manure and cover crops, which are used simply to boost short-run production of subsequent grain crops on level soil types, also are not true conservation practices.

The conservation payment program of the Production and Marketing Administration has largely failed to meet this first elementary efficiency test in conservation. Although the chief resource of the Soil Conservation Service, technical assistance, has been more largely devoted to true conservation practices, the Service has been increasingly guilty of devoting its technical assistance to jobs of a nonconservation nature. As the districts have spread out over areas where erosion has been less critical, a larger proportion of SCS technical time has been spent in developing irrigation systems, drainage facilities, and in improving rotations on level land. "Given the objective of maximum conservation," points out Heady, "the efforts of a farm planner in York County, Nebraska, for example, should be allocated to erosion control on the rough land rather than to irrigation development on level lands. Similarly, one farm planner in Champaign County, Illinois, concentrating on drainage and one in Switzerland County, Indiana, combating erosion would not represent the best use of resources." [4]

---

[3] Earl O. Heady, "Efficiency in Public Soil-Conservation Programs," *The Journal of Political Economy*, Vol. LIX, February, 1951, pp. 47–60.
[4] *Ibid.*, p. 51.

Secondly, public resources should be allocated between soil eroding areas on the basis of soil types. An acre of one soil subject to erosion should not necessarily have as much claim on public assistance as an acre of another soil subject to erosion. To obtain the greatest degree of conservation (that is, the smallest diminution in future production from given resource inputs) resource allocations should be made between soils subject to erosion on the basis of their marginal productivity in the relevant future time period. For example, Heady says:

> Limited conservation resources should have priority in preventing the loss of an acre of the excellent Tama-Muscatine soils of eastern Iowa over an acre of Shelby-Sharpsburg in southern Iowa or northern Missouri. . . . If annual conservation appropriations are limited and if diminution of future production is to be minimized, it is more important to save two acres of Marshall silt loam while two acres of Shelby silt loam erode away than to save one acre each of Marshall and Shelby while one acre of each also erodes away.[5]

Obviously, the Soil Conservation Service, working through the districts, has not allocated its technical assistance according to such a guide-line. Rather, the districts have scheduled assistance to farmers according to such criteria as time of farmer application for assistance, geographical location of farm, intensity of farmer interest in securing conservation assistance, membership of farmer in a natural neighborhod group which is ready to work on a group basis.

In the third place, according to the criterion of efficiency in the use of resources, public funds should be spent on those practices which yield the greatest degree of conservation per dollar invested. SCS technical assistance should thus be allocated among practices on the basis of productivity principals. Points out Heady:

> Widespread application of practices which have the greatest effect in erosion control and hence in preventing diminution of future production should be attained before resources are devoted to simple practices which have less relationship to potential future output. Yet farm planners have been occupied in devising complete plans for some farms while there were waiting lists of other farms to be planned even on the same soil association. Optimum allocation of limited technical assistance would require application of fewer but critical erosion control practices on greater numbers of farms rather than application of the greatest number of practices on fewer farms.[6]

---

[5] *Ibid.*, p. 51.
[6] *Ibid.*, p. 53.

The appraisal of a public soil conservation program according to the efficiency measurement raises challenging questions for those controlling public conservation policy. But as a measurement for evaluating the district as an instrumentality for achieving conservation, its usefulness is limited. Conservation policy is a question in political economy. It cannot be formulated in terms of economics alone. In the first place, it is unlikely that the American process of political decision would permit the establishment of a conservation program which allocated federal funds on a basis which might disqualify whole counties and even states from a share in them. Secondly, if it were possible to get such a program politically established, its social feasibility would be doubtful.

Although the proposal for making allocations for conservation work in accordance with the criterion of efficient use of resources recognizes such institutional obstacles as tenure arrangements, lack of capital, and economic instability, it does not have a solution for overcoming these obstacles. Moreover, it seemingly overlooks the human equation in conservation. It minimizes the psychology of the private agent — the farmer — who must be persuaded to carry out the preponderant share of the conservation job. Conservation priorities cannot run counter to his code of values, concepts of fairness and practicality, and habits of work. For a public conservation program, if it is to be executed, must stimulate millions of farmers to put their own energies and resources into the job. Indeed, without this use of private energy and resources for conservation, the expenditure of the limited public resources now available for district conservation would be comparatively unproductive.

Thus, the first advantage which the district may have over other types of governmental units in getting the conservation job done lies in its capacity to stimulate and harness private energies and resources for conservation. The district's governmental machinery permits it to accept, utilize, and bring into a common local action the energies and resources of individuals, groups, and governmental agencies with an interest in conservation.

The district's potential capacity to mobilize resources for conservation, however, is no guarantee that it will develop an effective conservation program. But the district has a second attribute which may give it capacity for executing the conservation job. In its mechanism, the district has at least the potential for selecting and blending the best thinking of each group in

Fig. 16 — A South Carolina farmstead before application of soil conservation measures.

Fig. 17 — Area shown in Fig. 16 after kudzu was established on Class VII land.

its effort to achieve the most effective conservation program. How effectively the district uses the resources at its disposal in carrying on the conservation work, of course, depends on its actual ability to select and use only the most suitable techniques and practices and administrative devices and procedures.

HARNESSING OF LOCAL ENERGIES AND RESOURCES

First, then, what has been the district's capacity to channel resources and energies into conservation? The resources and assistance which the federal government gives the district already have been sufficiently outlined to give an understanding of the peculiar advantage the district has over a local unit of government which is not set up to receive federal assistance. The question now is how successful has the district been in harnessing local and state energies and resources which would not likely be tapped if public conservation activity should come into the counties as the program of a federal agency alone.

Citizen passive acceptance of government regulation or service is often not sufficient in accomplishing the new tasks marked out as the public's responsibility. The thinking behind the development of the district device was that the federal government itself should not come into the counties either to compel or persuade farmers to join together in a collective, organized effort to fight the erosion of their lands.

District Use of Compulsory Land-Use Regulations

Although farmer participation in erosion control was to be sought largely through voluntary means, the federal Department of Agriculture believed that the governmental unit directly responsible for getting farmers to carry on conservation must have a police power to compel the recalcitrant minority of farmers to carry out erosion control. The early thinking of the leaders in federal soil conservation activity was dominated by a belief in the necessity for securing the complete conservation of all lands within a natural erosion area, if erosion control was to be effectively and permanently accomplished. Therefore, as long as conservation activity was organized upon a watershed basis, it seemed particularly necessary that the minority of non-cooperating farmers be forced to control their soils' erosion, lest the cooperating farmers be unable to control theirs.

From the standpoint of constitutionality the national government could not directly compel farmer compliance with conservation practices. The national lack of a police power, as such, necessitated federal reliance upon the state's exercise of that power in some manner. Too, the pragmatic advantages of using local farmers for the formulating and enforcing of rules to regulate the conduct of their neighbors could not be ignored. The creation of soil conservation districts, as political subdivisions of the state, was held as the most suitable means of exercising last resort compulsion. Thus far, however, the district has not, with very few exceptions, served as an agency of compulsion in conservation administration.

The Standard State Soil Conservation Districts Law calls for a delegation of the state's police power to enable districts to enact and enforce land-use regulations governing the district in the interest of conserving soil and soil resources and preventing and controlling soil erosion. But such regulations cannot be enacted into law unless a majority of the land occupiers voting in a referendum favor the enactment. Amendment or repeal likewise may be effected only after referendum approval. Regulations may include requirements for such engineering operations as construction of terraces, dams and dikes, etc.; requirements for special cropping methods such as strip, contouring, lister furrowing, etc.; requirements for specified programs and tillage practices, such as crop rotations; and requirements that highly erosive land be retired from cultivation.[7]

Enforcement provisions are carefully calculated to allow flexibility, to obviate undue hardship and to stay within constitutional bounds.[8] Violation of a regulation is punishable by fine as a misdemeanor. Further, any land occupier sustaining damage by failure of any other land occupier to abide by regulations may sue to recover damages from the offender, provided this procedure is authorized by the ordinance. Finally, the supervisors may petition the courts for an order permitting them to go upon the land of the offender, do the necessary work, and collect from him the costs thus incurred. A board of adjustment must be established in any district which adopts land-use regulations. Acting on petition by any land occupier, the board may permit individual variances from the land-use regulation, whenever it appears that a strict application of the regulation would cause

---

[7] Standard Act, *op. cit.*, Sec. 9.

[8] The Standard Act, pp. 31–64, contains a very thorough abstract, prepared by the Solicitor of the United States Department of Agriculture, supporting the constitutionality of the act.

". . . great practical difficulties or unnecessary hardship." The board of adjustment's decisions are reviewable by the courts.[9]

Despite the emphasis which the Service from the beginning has placed on the power to adopt land-use regulations, this power is not provided in the laws of sixteen states.[10] Among the thirty-two states which authorize districts to adopt land-use regulations, there are wide variations in requirements for adoption. The majority referendum vote required ranges from 51 to 90 per cent. Further, as shown in Table 1, ten states make enactment of regulations more difficult by such additional provisions as the requirement that the vote also must represent a stipulated percentage of the district's acreage, that a certain percentage of those eligible to vote must participate, or that the state soil conservation committee's approval must be had, and so forth.[11] Only six states follow the Standard Act in requiring only a simple majority of votes cast in order to adopt a regulation.[12] Only ten states follow the Standard Act in permitting non-owner operators to vote in the referendum.[13] Finally, only three states — Maryland, Nevada and Utah — follow the Standard Act on both important features of percentage of vote required and voting eligibility.

No trend in state enabling legislation has been as definite as the trend away from granting the land-use regulation power to the district. All twenty-two states which passed soil conservation districts laws in 1937 granted this power.[14] Of the four state laws enacted in 1938,[15] only California ommitted the land-use regulations feature. Her law was re-enacted in 1940 to include that power, but it was again deleted by a 1949 amendment. Of the ten laws passed in 1939,[16] only Idaho and Iowa failed to give districts this power.

[9] *Ibid.*, Secs. 10–12.
[10] Arizona, California, Connecticut, Delaware, Idaho, Indiana, Iowa, Maine, Massachusetts, Michigan, Missouri, New Hampshire, New York, Ohio, Pennsylvania, and Rhode Island.
[11] These states are Georgia, Kentucky, Mississippi, New Jersey, New Mexico, Oregon, South Dakota, Texas, West Virginia, and Wyoming.
[12] Florida, Georgia, Maryland, Nevada, Utah, and Vermont.
[13] Kansas, Maryland, Minnesota, Montana, Nevada, North Dakota, South Dakota, Utah, Virginia, and Wyoming.
[14] Arkansas, Colorado, Florida, Georgia, Illinois, Indiana, Kansas, Maryland, Michigan, Minnesota, Nebraska, Nevada, New Jersey, New Mexico, North Carolina, North Dakota, Oklahoma, Pennsylvania, South Carolina, South Dakota, Utah, and Wisconsin.
[15] California, Mississippi, Virginia, and Louisiana.
[16] Alabama, Idaho, Iowa, Montana, Oregon, Tennessee, Texas, Vermont, Washington, and West Virginia.

TABLE 1

PROVISIONS OF STATE LAWS CONCERNING LAND-USE REGULATIONS, JANUARY 1, 1952*

(X = Yes)

State	Districts Authorized to Adopt Land-use Regulation	Eligibility for Voting in Referendum		Percentage of Votes Cast Necessary for Adoption of Ordinance
		Owners	Owners and Non-owner Operators	
Alabama	X	X		80
Arizona				
Arkansas	X	X		75
California				
Colorado	X	X		75
Connecticut				
Delaware				
Florida	X	X		51
Georgia	X	X		51†
Idaho				
Illinois	X	X		75
Indiana				
Iowa				
Kansas	X		X	90
Kentucky	X	X		90‡
Louisiana	X	X		67
Maine				
Maryland	X		X	51
Massachusetts				
Michigan				
Minnesota	X		X	85
Mississippi	X	X		67§
Missouri				
Montana	X		X	65
Nebraska	X	X		75
Nevada	X		X	51
New Hampshire				
New Jersey	X	‖		‖
New Mexico	X	X		67¶
New York				
North Carolina	X	X		67
North Dakota	X		X	75
Ohio				
Oklahoma	X	X		90
Oregon	X	X		75**
Pennsylvania				
Rhode Island				
South Carolina	X	X		67
South Dakota	X		X	67††
Tennessee	X	X		67
Texas	X	X‡‡		90
Utah	X		X	51
Vermont	X	X		51
Virginia	X		X	67
Washington	X	X		67
West Virginia	X	X		60§§
Wisconsin	X	X		67
Wyoming	X		X	75‖‖

In contrast, of the twelve state laws enacted since 1939,[17] only Kentucky and Wyoming provided for the land-use regulatory power. None of the six state laws passed since 1941 provides for this power. Further, in 1945, Indiana, Michigan and Pennsylvania deleted the land-use regulation power by amending their original laws. California followed suit in 1949. Finally, in 1945 and 1947 respectively, Colorado and Oklahoma amended their original laws to make the adoption of land-use regulations a great deal more difficult. They raised the referendum voting requirement from 51 per cent to 75 per cent and 90 per cent respectively.

So far the land-use regulation power has been little used by the districts throughout the country. Only ten districts — one in North Dakota, one in Oregon, and eight in Colorado — have land-use ordinances in effect.

A brief comparative summary of the provisions of these ordinances might be useful as a case study of the nature of land-use regulations. These ordinances include grazing regulations, prohibition against breaking out sod or brush land, requirements for vegetative and mechanical control of wind erosion, restriction of traffic over stabilized sand dunes, and prohibition of any other land uses which would seriously deteriorate the ground cover on stabilized dunes. As shown in Table 3, some of the districts have more than one type of ordinance.

The ordinances of four Colorado districts prohibit the break-

---

[17] Kentucky and New York, in 1940; Arizona, Maine, Ohio, and Wyoming, in 1941; Delaware, Missouri, and Rhode Island, in 1943; Connecticut, Massachusetts, and New Hampshire, in 1945.

---

* *See* Appendix A, for legal citations.

† Approval of proposed regulation by the state soil conservation committee is a prerequisite to holding referendum.

‡ Also provides that regulation cannot be adopted, "unless landowners voting to enact . . . proposed ordinance own at least eighty per cent of the land in the districts."

§ Requires approval of two-thirds of all landowners owning at least two-thirds of the lands affected by the regulation.

‖ No referendum provided. Regulations will be operative unless owners of twenty-five per cent of acreage in district file objection.

¶ If any landowner objects to a land-use ordinance, it shall not be operative against him unless fifty per cent of the owners of "agricultural land" or "grazing land" (depending on which is affected) approve the ordinance in writing.

** Must represent two-thirds of land within the district. Approval of the state soil conservation committee is also required.

†† Must also "represent at least two-thirds of the land area of the district."

‡‡ Must also be resident of a county included in the district, and twenty-one years of age.

§§ State soil conservation committee approval is also necessary.

‖‖ Provides for separate balloting for "owners" and "occupiers." Requires three-fourths majority of votes cast by each group and three-fourths of acreage voted.

ing out for crop production of additional sod or brush land except upon the approval of the district board of supervisors. Several of the ordinances provide that land out of cultivation during any three-year period ending after the regulation was adopted cannot be cropped again without the approval of the supervisors. In considering an application to plow up such land, the supervisors are to be guided by the land-use capability classification of the land in question. The classification is based upon such considerations as soil type, native fertility, degree of slope, degree of existing or threatened erosion, and other specified factors.

TABLE 2
SOIL CONSERVATION DISTRICTS WHICH HAVE LAND-USE ORDINANCES IN EFFECT,
JANUARY 1, 1952

District	Acres	Farms
Cedar, North Dakota......................	306,880	144
Warrenton-Dune, Oregon...................	5,468	19
Big Sandy, Colorado......................	242,912	282
Cheyenne, Colorado.......................	592,012	272
Horse-Rush Creek, Colorado.	288,075	198
Northeast Prowers, Colorado..............	277,476	490
Plainview, Colorado......................	150,724	153
Southeastern Baca, Colorado..............	393,120	309
Timpas, Colorado.........................	566,404	475
Two Buttes, Colorado.....................	91,239	60

All lands in these districts have been placed in one of the following classifications:

Class I—Lands suitable for cultivation without special practices
Class II—Lands suitable for cultivation with simple practices
Class III—Lands suitable for cultivation with complex or intensive practices
Class IV—Lands not wholly suitable for regular cultivation but which, with adequate protection, are suitable for cultivation in limited acreages subject to complex or intensive practices
Class V—Lands not suitable for cultivation because slightly susceptible to deterioration, but suitable for permanent vegetation for grazing or woodland use without special practices or measures
Class VI—Lands not suitable for cultivation and moderately susceptible to deterioration, but suitable for grazing through the use of special practices and good range management
Class VII—Lands not suitable for cultivation and highly susceptible to deterioration, but suitable for grazing through the use of special practices and good range management

Class VIII—Barren or waste lands, not suitable for any agricultural use[18]

Upon receipt of an owner's application to plow or cultivate land, the supervisors must approve the application if the land in question belongs in Class I, II, or III. If it belongs in Class IV, V, VI, VII, or VIII, the supervisors must disapprove the application unless they determine that such disapproval would cause great practical difficulties or unnecessary hardship, in which case they must for that reason grant a variance from the requirement of this regulation.

TABLE 3

TYPES OF LAND-USE REGULATIONS IN EFFECT IN SOIL CONSERVATION DISTRICTS, JANUARY 1, 1952

	Type of Land-Use Ordinance			
Name of District	Sod land regulation	Blow land regulation	Grazing regulation	Sand dune erosion control
Cedar, North Dakota.........	....	....	X	....
Warrenton-Dune, Oregon.....	....	....	....	X
Big Sandy, Colorado.........	X	X	....	....
Cheyenne, Colorado..........	....	X	....	....
Horse-Rush Creek, Colorado...	X	X	....	....
Northeast Prowers, Colorado...	....	X	....	....
Plainview, Colorado..........	X	....	....	....
Southeastern Baca, Colorado...	....	X	....	....
Timpas, Colorado............	X	....	....	....
Two Buttes, Colorado.........	....	X	....	....

Blow land regulations are in effect in six Colorado districts. Typically, these regulations provide that:

Whenever the board of supervisors shall determine that soil is blowing from the land of one owner to that of another, notice shall be sent by registered mail to the owner, agent or occupant of the land from which such soil is blowing, requiring such owner to immediately take the necessary steps to prevent such blowing.

In case of non-compliance, the supervisors are authorized to perform the necessary work and certify the costs incurred to the county commissioners for collection as taxes against the offending land. Under most of these ordinances, the supervisors are empowered to grant a variance from the requirements, in case the strict application of the regulation would work a great hardship on the petitioning owner or occupant.

---

[18] Quoted from Horse-Rush Creek Conservation District Ordinance.

The grazing regulation of the Cedar District, North Dakota, limits the number of livestock grazed to the prescribed carrying capacity of the land. Three Colorado districts, all located in Baca County, had grazing regulations at one time or another. According to a soils specialist at Colorado A. & M. College, these regulations were, for all practical purposes, dead issues by May, 1945, before the Colorado legislature nullified them.[19]

In 1948, the Warrenton-Dune District in Oregon enacted two ordinances designed to control the use of former sand dunes that had been stilled and re-claimed through the planting of beach grass and shore pine. According to the executive secretary of the Oregon State Soil Conservation Committee, these ordinances affect only a minor portion of the distict.[20] A variety of measures are provided for protecting the specified areas. Livestock grazing is restricted, all types of traffic are limited to hard surfaced roads or trails, and other deteriorating land uses are outlawed.

Colorado's experience with land-use regulations has been a dramatic one. A bitter controversy among the landowners in three districts wound up in the state legislature. After much debate, the Colorado legislature amended its soil conservation districts law, in 1945, to require that land-use ordinances could not be adopted unless 75 per cent (formerly 51 per cent) of the votes cast at a referendum were favorable. Through its provision that votes may be cast either in person or by proxy, this amendment also makes it possible for non-residents to participate in the referendum.

The amendment nullified, after 45 days from its effective date, all land-use regulations previously adopted, unless, in the interim, they were readopted in accordance with the new procedure. In three districts in which land-use regulations had never been seriously opposed, the ordinances were readopted without difficulty.[21] As indicated by Table 3, since that time five additional districts have adopted ordinances designed to discourage the bringing into crop production of submarginal land during the postwar wheat boom.

The strained atmosphere of charges and counter-charges surrounding the Colorado legislative deliberations in 1945, and the subsequent attempts to re-enact the invalidated ordinances in a

---

[19] Dale S. Romine, "Land Use Ordinance Experiences in Colorado," 1950, p. 1.
[20] Letter from Howard E. Cushman to author, July 16, 1951.
[21] Romine, "Land Use Ordinance Experiences in Colorado," *op. cit.*, p. 1.

few districts, illustrate well the explosive potentialities of the land-use regulations power. The proponents of status quo in land-use regulations — and the soil conservation district supervisors formed the nucleus of this group — charged that land speculators and non-residents were intent on making huge wartime profits through expanded cultivation of erodible lands, even at the risk of precipitating future dust storms. The enemies of land-use regulations — and this group was spearheaded by the Eastern Colorado Improvement Association — charged the supervisors with "dictatorship, un-Americanism, unpatriotic suppression of production, denying a farmer the right to farm his own land," and the like.

Landowners did not lack for public reporting of the issues involved in land-use ordinance readoption. County affiliates of the Eastern Colorado Improvement Association took the fight to the people through the medium of full-page purchased advertisements in the local newspapers. District supervisors sought to follow suit, but their frequency in making the news was somewhat hampered by their lack of funds, and by the resulting necessity of having to rely largely upon local business concerns to purchase the requisite newspaper space. The Association quite openly courted the favor of the non-resident landowners, whose voting proxy its president evidently succeeded in becoming. According to the Association, the supervisors likewise sought the good will of the non-residents, whose interests had hitherto not concerned the supervisors.

The following excerpts from advertisements typify the tack taken by the Eastern Colorado Improvement Association in its war against the land-use ordinances. One such advertisement in the June 7, 1945, issue of the *Cheyenne Wells (Colorado) Record* appeared under the sponsorship of the Cheyenne County Improvement Association, and carried the parent association's appealing omnibus slogan: "For progress — for prosperity — for harmony — for true conservation — against selfishness — against bickering — against bureaucracy . . . local, state and national." This advertisement exhorted landowners, thus:

This is your opportunity to break the shackles that have retarded the growth, development and prosperity of the eastern half of Cheyenne County. You can do this by voting against these unfair, un-American, dictatorial rules that prevent land owners from using their own land. Before these land use rules were adopted, land owners had "marketable title" to their land. Now, through no action of their own,

no matter how long they have been paying taxes, a serious encumbrance
has been placed on their titles. They simply cannot farm their land unless they have farmed it during the past three years. . . . When a hungry
world is asking for bread and meat is not the time to preach the doctrine of scarcity advocated by the proponents of these land use rules!
All we ask is that other folks can use our good land as directors of the
Soil Erosion District use it themselves. They raise cattle and sheep,
corn, wheat, barley and maize. They, as individuals, raise a lot of these
things! But as members of the Soil Erosion District they deny other land
owners the right to develop their land in the same way. Just because
they were fortunate enough to acquire some of the land that has been
under cultivation for a long time is no reason why they should deny
others the privilege of plowing enough of their land so that they, too,
can establish homes and make a living out of their investment. . . . The
Cheyenne County Improvement Association is a non-profit association
consisting of farmers, business and professional people. We are working
to build up our Community. We want better and more farms, better
business conditions, better towns, better roads.

In the same vein, an advertisement, sponsored by the Kit
Carson County Improvement Association, and appearing in the
June 14, 1945, issue of *The Burlington Record,* pleaded:

For your own freedom, for the freedom of your land, and to help
save the freedom of your good old U.S.A., let us get busy on the HOME
FRONT and vote against the re-adoption of the land use rules. During
the depression, a "Soil Erosion District" was organized for the purpose
of having authority to control wind erosion. However, since its organization, the district has gotten into the control of a group who are using
it for purposes other than that for which it was first intended. For
example, they have passed "Land Use Rules and Regulations" by which
a Board of Supervisors can and do stop land owners from farming their
own land. They even have a regulation that any field which has not
been farmed for three years cannot be farmed without the consent of
the board. (And you can see that it might be possible if the land is
located near some particular person that they might not permit it to
be farmed as forced idleness makes it of little value and some particular
person might be able to buy or rent it for little or nothing.) . . . You
and we, as land owners, would like to see your land and our land free
to be operated as you or we think best.

In rebuttal, and in contrastingly restrained tones, the supervisors of Cheyenne Soil Erosion District spoke through an advertisement in the June 14, 1945, issue of the *Cheyenne Wells (Colorado) Record:*

Land Use Regulations now seem to be the most discussed subject
of the day. Regulations of any kind are generally the result of some
abuse or excess. Speed, sanitary, building — any regulation, in fact
— becomes necessary because people are inclined to excesses. Stop-lights

in any well regulated city, at railroad crossings, are only warnings to the public that danger exists. To disregard them is only to court danger. All these things are not to make your course more difficult. They are for YOUR PROTECTION. . . . Land Use Ordinances in your Cheyenne Soil Erosion District are also the result of excesses. Excessive breaking of sod land, regardless of whether the land was suitable for crop or range. These regulations, like the stop-light, do not stop you from farming, as you have been told; they only insist that you proceed in an orderly manner to protect you and your neighbor who expect to stay here, from a repetition of the "Dust Bowl" days.

Feelings ran so high that an objective accounting of happenings in Colorado in those days is difficult to find. Journalist Roscoe Fleming, who interviewed residents of Cheyenne Wells soon after the unsuccesful attempt to readopt the land-use regulations in that district, gave the following report:

The 1945 Colorado Legislature, under heavy pressure by land speculators and representatives of absentee owners, repealed all soil conservation regulations and provided that new ones could be adopted only by a vote of 75 per cent of the landowners, including absentee owners who could vote by proxy.

. . . in eastern Colorado the land was owned largely by people from Cape Cod to San Diego whose only interest in it was to get a profit. Assiduous local agents collected proxies.

Let Mrs. M. D. Brakeman, editor of a local weekly, who has lived here since 1916, describe what happened: "To make it absolutely legal, proxies had to be voted singly. There were less than 300 resident landowners in the district, and there were 634 tracts held by non-residents. Some of the agents had collected 20 or 30 proxies apiece. It made us sick to watch them walk around the table, dropping a proxy vote in the box at each circuit. When it was all over we had gone back to the bad old days."

There is some resentment against the non-residents. Said Rel Morrow of Burlington: "If the dust comes, all they have to do is to let their hired hands go and they don't have to worry much about eating dust, back in a nice comfortable apartment in New York. If they are lucky, they've realized enough from one or two crops to pay out and make a profit, anyway." [22]

The Colorado experience is valuable, because it reveals the type of attack to which land-use regulations might be subjected in other states attempting to enact them. The possibilities for capitalizing upon misinformation concerning land-use regulation procedures, and the odds against which the proponents of an ordinance would have to fight, are quite evident.

Even more important, the attack on land-use regulations in

---

[22] Roscoe Fleming, "Absentee Owners Clean Up: Dust-Devils Marching on High Plains Again As Proxy Plows Bite," *The Washington Post*, September 8, 1946, p. 3B.

Colorado is useful in concretely explaining why a locally-governed district was held by the fashioners of the district device to be the most feasible means for securing compulsory conservation. The Colorado experience seems to demonstrate: First, that land-use regulations can be effected only by giving the freedom to make such determination to local people, who have a live and vivid daily reminder of the need for mandatory erosion control. Secondly, that state-wide compulsory regulations could probably never be adopted, because the forces which could not control particular local areas can oftentimes develop sufficient strength at the state level to shape state action. The Colorado experience raises the question of whether such forces pressing at the state level will always permit the exercising of genuine local determination, through the district device, when adoption of land-use regulations seems immient in local areas.

Outside of Colorado, North Dakota, and Oregon, the actual adoption of land-use regulations seems to have been seriously contemplated in only a very few scattered districts. As mentioned earlier, the supervisors of Southside District, Virginia, jumped the gun by stating in their 1942 annual report that the supervisors were willing to take the first steps toward compulsory conservation. But they specifically retracted in their next annual report. The Oklahoma Extension Soil Conservationist reported in 1946 that two districts in that state had become interested in land-use regulations. The 1947 amendment of Oklahoma's soil conservation districts law, which raised the referendum majority requirement from 51 per cent to 90 per cent, follows the Colorado pattern. An ounce of prevention was applied on the state level, and the latent threat of ordinances in two local areas was forestalled.

Despite the general disinclination to resort to compulsory conservation, a final verdict on the future usefulness of land-use regulations cannot yet be given. Soil conservation districts and their programs were too new to be very well understood before World War II. Then with the war came numerous controls on individual actions, imposed from above. Released from wartime regulations, citizens were not eager to accept new ones.

Once again, with the Korean crisis, the national emphasis has been on production. Rightly or wrongly, the drive for production tends to divert popular attention from serious thought of compulsory conservation. Finally, farmers have been making money. They have not felt the pinch of competition. This is never a conducive atmosphere for the acceptance of controls, self-imposed or otherwise. An established and long-accepted police power restriction on farm operations would have been severely strained. Any effort to impose an unaccustomed control, such as land-use regulations enforced through the medium of a new and untried political institution, could expect little support.

Aside from the factors of the newness of the district device and the unpropitious economic climate, still another development has probably deterred adoption of land-use regulations. Because of the strong trend from the watershed to the county as the basis for district organization, compulsory conservation may have lost some of its practical importance. Compulsory conservation was to be a last resort method of securing the complete and unified conservation treatment of an entire watershed. Since most district administrative areas no longer correspond with watersheds, the hope for securing the originally sought uniform watershed treatment, either by voluntary or compulsory means, has noticeably dimmed.

In suspending its categories of assistance, the SCS has forfeited an effective prod in obtaining legislative authorization for land-use regulations. Nevertheless, the Service still envisions the future possible necessity for compulsory conservation. In 1947, the SCS released to its field staff a pamphlet entitled "Land Use Regulations in Soil Conservation Districts." In the foreword by the SCS Chief, it is carefully explained: "This pamphlet has been prepared as a reference to aid in understanding the regulatory authority of soil conservation districts. It is not intended to encourage or discourage the use of that authority." [23] Despite this detached tone, the mere preparation and release of the pamphlet is proof enough that the Service does not consider land-use regulations a dead issue. If dust storms and economic depression again team up, the Service believes that farmers will want to adopt land-use ordinances. Against that day, SCS is advising that the authorization for land-use regulations be retained in the state statutes.

District as an Agency of Persuasion

Although the district was seen as an instrument for exercising compulsion in conservation, it was chiefly viewed as a device for developing a maximum of local farmer initiative and responsibility in conserving local soils. If public conservation activity

---

[23] Philip M. O'Brien, Thomas L. Gaston and Tom Dale, "Land Use Regulations in Soil Conservation Districts," SCS, January 1947.

came into a county as the program of a federal agency, local farmers, it was felt, would probably adopt a subsidy psychology, expecting the government to do the conserving of their lands for them. But the SCS conservation program was designed primarily to give technical service to farmers who were willing to use their own labor and material resources in preventing the erosion of their lands. It was felt that farmer initiative, responsibility, and reliance upon their own resources could best be challenged if conservation activity was organized around independent units of local government, which farmers themselves managed and controlled.

The first problem, then, in developing the district into a mechanism for harnessing local famers' energies for soil conservation is — as the Virginia Extension conservationist puts it — convincing the local people that the district belongs to them. This, he feels, is the biggest task confronting all today.

As yet, farmers have not entirely understood that the district is a unit of their local government. Over and over, in all sections of the country, rural people reveal that they have not caught the conception of the district as a local institution. As the Michigan state committee observes in a newsletter: ". . . it is common knowledge that there are a lot of farmers even in our older districts who still don't know what their soil conservation district is, who the directors are, or what is being done."

Frequently the board of supervisors is thought of as just another committee. "Too many people are confused between districts, the ACP program, and SCS," observes a New England state conservationist. This confusion has been found to exist in all sections of the country. Most commonly the district is misidentified with the Soil Conservation Service. Districts are still quite generally referred to as Soil Conservation *Service* districts. Sometimes the board of supervisors is seen as a sort of advisory committee for Service personnel.

Too often only a few farmers in a district are found to be familiar with the district's governing body, although many may know the Service's technicians. In short, although an understanding of the need for soil conservation has been established in the popular mind in all sections of the country, farmers generally do not yet recognize the district as the responsible unit in community conservation.

The problem, the Service staff recognizes, is to build up an adequate understanding of the district as the government in the conservation program. The state conservationist in Vermont summed up general Service opinion when he declared:

> People should know that districts are set up under State law and run by the local people. They should know that the role of the Soil Conservation Service is to assist districts in carrying out whatever program they have adopted. . . . They should know something about their policies and procedures. . . . Even these things are not enough. District cooperators especially, but others too, need to be kept informed of the current activities of districts. This is especially important from the standpoint of keeping sustained interest in their district.[24]

The most common method suggested for creating community recognition of the district as a local governmental unit is an educational campaign of meetings, pictures, exhibits, newspaper publicity, and so on. Too frequently in the past, the district and its supervisors have not been identified in Service posters showing conservation needs and accomplishments. But, increasingly, effort is being made to project the district in such publicity. For example, the Michigan state committee declares:

> It seems that one of our big jobs is to advertise our district to farmers and others. . . . I suggest that we make the topic, "How Can We Do a Better Job Advertising our Soil Conservation District" the chief item for discussion at one of our Board meetings or perhaps at a regional Directors' meeting. . . . Just the other day I saw a picture in the Benton Harbor paper of the St. Joe River District Board in session. There was a nice little story about the working of the district along with it. Mighty good advertising.

More effective than publicity campaigns in publicizing the district are the previously discussed daily strategies in the routine of conservation administration, which aid in farmer identification of the district. The first of these strategies is the holding of board meetings in a place which is identified with community affairs — such as the school, courthouse, town hall, or church — rather than in the local SCS office.

The use of stationery with a district letterhead, with the names of the governing body printed upon it, also is suggested as a method of building up the district and the governing body in farmers' minds. The great majority of districts now have their own letterheads.

Supervisor contact with farmers is clearly the most effective means of creating farmer awareness of the supervisors as the ad-

---

[24] "Talk to County Agents in Vermont," at the County Agents Annual Conference, December, 1947.

ministrators of the district. But it is almost as important for professional employees, in their work with the district's farmers, to emphasize the supervisors as the managers of the district. As the supervisors of the Southside District, Virginia, put it in an annual report:

> We believe that the Soil Conservation Service personnel can help the Supervisors in their administrative work by acknowledging the district and its work when they contact farmers.

Perhaps in response to this suggestion, the Virginia Extension conservationist, as administrative officer of the state committee, sent out newsletters to 850 agricultural workers in organized districts, urging workers to assist in projecting the district program as that of local landowners, and explaining the correct terms for use in discussing districts. A follow-up letter was then sent to supervisors exhorting them to make their district a local organization:

> Workers of agencies cooperating with you must emphasize the district as a local organization of landowners. Every farmer contact should mean that more people know that this is the farmer's program and not one of the State or Federal governments.

In their work with farmers, professional workers are constantly to emphasize that all decisions upon the farmer's relationships with the district are to be made by the governing body. For example, it is to be the board which informs the farmer when the technician will aid him in planning his farm or in assisting him to begin applying his plan, and when conservation equipment will be routed to his farm. District correspondence, the Service constantly admonishes, should never be signed by Service personnel.

In the early days of the district program, Service workers took an aggressive part in drumming up farmer interest in conservation so that a favorable farmer referendum on the organization of a district might be obtained. A former district conservationist in Illinois describes how, in organizing his district, he and the county agent made a house-to-house canvass to secure votes. But the Service soon specifically forbade its field personnel thus to work in the organization of a district:

> The personnel of the Soil Conservation Service within the State may not act as agents of the State Soil Conservation Committee in connection with the organization of districts without the specific approval of the Secretary. This approval will ordinarily not be given unless the circumstances are most unusual, and the reasons should be obvious. If

the district's program is to be regarded as a State program in fact as well as in the theory, the State Committee must assume its own responsibilities, and the Service's role should be confined to that of a cooperator.[25]

From his vantage point in the Region III office, the above-mentioned former district conservationist observes that he now "knows of no district where an SCS man has carried on such an organizing program" as he had done in earlier days. Such organization work by Service personnel quite naturally introduced the conservation program to local people as a federal agricultural program rather than one belonging to their own community.

Original popular farmer understanding and support of the district as a local government controlled by local officials is to be achieved, then, through widespread farmer participation in the organizing of the district. In Virginia, the Extension conservationist reports:

> Operating Districts have shown conclusively, that the more farmers participate and actually organize the District themselves, the better they understand the true meaning of a District and therefore the operation is easier. . . . A concerted effort is being made to secure more farmer participation in the actual organization of the District. . . . The State Committee does not feel that sufficient farmer participation has been secured but insists that the organization of the District be put clearly before the farmers.

The Colorado Extension conservationist early reported that: ". . . we have insisted that the decision to organize districts be made by the local people and they do the actual circulating of petitions and other fundamental work not of an educational nature." Seemingly, with the Secretary of Agriculture's 1951 reorganization order, the official SCS policy of keeping its personnel in the background during the organization of districts has been abandoned. For the Secretary's memorandum specifically states:

> The PMA State Committee and the State Conservationist of the Soil Conservation Service shall jointly encourage the creation and development of Soil Conservation Districts.[26]

This may constitute nothing more than an official recognition of the important role that Department of Agriculture employees have necessarily played in stimulating district organization.

---

[25] "Suggestions for Consideration Concerning Cooperation with Soil Conservation Districts," from J. Phil Campbell, Chief, Division of Cooperative Planning and Relations, to Regional Conservators and State Coordinators, April 25, 1939. District Cooperation Series, Memorandum No. 11, p. 1.

[26] Secretary of Agriculture, Memorandum No. 1278, *op. cit.*, p. 3.

There is no more effective device for creating within citizens the knowledge that a unit of government is primarily theirs to manage and control than the mechanics of popular voting, whether in referenda or in the selection of governing officials. However, statistics on the frequency of elections and popular participation in voting reveal that the use of this device is far from sufficient. Another means of spreading popular understanding of the district through farmer participation is using farmer committees in the preparation of the district's program and work plan. Service personnel are increasingly encouraging the use of these farmer committees. The Region IV office insists that such committees be used in preparing programs and work plans. In some Texas districts, as many as one hundred farmers have participated in developing these documents.

Not only must local farmers be made aware of the district as a unit of their local government, but the district itself must develop methods and techniques for selling its program to farmers. Tours, annual meetings of district farmers, field days, demonstration projects, newspaper publicity, annual reports to district farmers, educational meetings, and talks by supervisors before other community organizations are all devices designed to awaken farmers' awareness of the need for carrying on conservation.

The most valuable social mechanism at the disposal of such a local unit as the district is, according to many in the Service organization, the *group action* process. It is the opinion of the former chief of the Soil Conservation Service that:

> One of the promising aspects of soil conservation districts is their peculiar capacity for utilizing group action to get work done on the land. This enormous potentiality for getting effective work done, not only in planning but in applying conservation plans to farms, and maintaining the work, is being used to advantage more and more. The excellent results we have had through this medium speak strongly for its further use on a rapidy increasing scale.[27]

The assistant chief of the Service told the House Subcommittee on Agricultural Appropriations that: ". . . the organization of conservation groups is one of the forward steps which has been taken by districts in organizing the local people to do their part of the job." [28]

The group action process follows the pattern of organizing farmers into work groups upon the basis of *natural* neighborhoods

[27] *Report of the Chief of the Soil Conservation Service,* 1946, p. 17.
[28] House Appropriation *Hearings,* 1947, *op. cit.,* p. 1004.

and communities. The procedure is for farmers within a small, natural social area to be called together by a farm leader in the area. During a series of educational and planning meetings, sponsored by the group leader, the Service technicians explain the land capability classes and various simple conservation practices. Special effort is made to point out things a farmer can do, without technical assistance, in advance of intensive treatment of his farm. The technicians explain the value of such practices as mowing weedy pastures, planting protective cover crops, preventing woodland fires, utilizing farm manures, planting trees or grass on critically steep land, and applying ground limestone to acid lands.

When farmers work together on their conservation problems in these *natural* social units, they will, according to the proponents of group action, not only work more vigorously and with less assistance from the technicians in applying the needed conservation measures, but they are more apt adequately to maintain the practices established. For they not only get a better understanding of what they can accomplish through soil conservation, but their interest in carrying out the work is strengthened by knowing they are working together with their neighbors in a community effort.

The community leader is the key person in selling a neighborhood of farmers upon carrying out a neighborhood conservation program. It is he who calls his neighbors together, acts as chairman of the educational and planning meetings, informs farmers through personal contacts on the value of group action, and urges them to carry through on their conservation undertakings.

District Use of State and Local Resources

The Service has sometimes been criticized as seeing in the local supervisors only extra hands for carrying out its bidding. According to H. H. Bennett, the district device has had much success in developing a corps of local workers for carrying district operations to farmers.

Probably never before in the history of this or any other country has there existed such a large and active body of volunteer, unpaid agricultural leaders as in this force of soil conservation district supervisors, directors, and other district officials.[29]

Perhaps Chief Bennett was overly optimistic in his estimation. But certainly, in addition to pulling into their administrative

---

[29] H. H. Bennett, "Soil Conservation — A Dream Coming True," address under auspices of Brown Creek Soil Conservation District, Wadesboro, North Carolina, September 9, 1946, p. 7.

work some 12,000 district supervisors, the districts have also brought to their operational assistance several thousand other farmers who, on the same unpaid basis, act as assistant supervisors. The use of assistant supervisors has often been tied directly in with the group action program. The community leaders become the assistant supervisors of their areas. In addition to selling the program to his neighbors, the group leader is to handle the mechanical arrangements for group meetings, help farmers install simple practices, help schedule the use of machinery in his area, keep a record of conservation practices applied, and so on. The chief of the Service reported as early as 1941 that by using the assistant supervisors it was found that the staffs of the soil conservation districts could project their influence and assistance into more communities at a more rapid pace.[30]

To what degree the assistant supervisors actually have worked at district affairs cannot, of course, be estimated. The noticeable reluctance of the supervisors themselves to carry on the routine, menial administrative work of the district would indicate, however, that assistant supervisors might be willing to devote even less time to district affairs.

In addition to their corps of volunteer, unpaid workers, some districts, through their own resources or from state allocations, are employing administrative staffs. Here the districts are definitely implementing the conservation program with real administrative assistance. The most general type of staff assistance the district employs is a district clerk or bookkeeper who handles correspondence and keeps records and accounts. Sometimes two or three neighboring districts pool their resources to hire a bookkeeper jointly.

In an increasing number of districts an operations manager, district manager, equipment manager, or superintendent is being employed. His job is usually to supervise the routing, moving, and repair of equipment, to make farmer contacts for arrangements for materials, such as fertilizers, seed, posts, lumber for headgates, and to perform other routine administrative tasks which neither the supervisors nor the technicians have time to perform. The practice of employing, on a part-time basis, one of the district supervisors to carry out the routine work of the district is being adopted in several states. In addition, of course, the districts employ machine operators to work SCS- or district-owned equipment. Increasingly, the districts also are employing conservation

---

[30] *Report of the Chief of the Soil Conservation Service,* 1941, p. 13.

aids, sub-professional local men, who, under the direction of the Service technicians, assist in the laying out of terrace lines, and so on. Probably one of the most significant trends towards district independence in conservation activity is the growth of such full-time, paid district staffs.

MATERIAL ASSISTANCE OF COUNTY AND STATE IN CONSERVATION ACTIVITY

A variety of county and township material assistance to districts is authorized in the laws of several states. Included among the several states which specifically authorize county appropriations for general district operations are California, Maryland, Minnesota, New York, and Pennsylvania. States with laws specifying that county equipment may be made available for district use include Colorado, Minnesota, New York, and Wisconsin. The services of county officials, such as the county attorney, is granted to districts in laws of several states, including Oklahoma, Minnesota, and New York. This does not imply that county and township assistance to districts is not permitted in other states. For the general or implied powers of local governments are oftentimes sufficiently broad to include such cooperation. Even when this may not be the case, it is probable that county or township lending of equipment to districts, on a small scale, is going unchallenged.

No comprehensive statistics on the amount of county or township assistance given districts have ever been prepared. District annual reports give neither consistent nor complete coverage on this item. Nor are figures available from state soil conservation committees or any level of SCS administration. Gleanings from numerous sources, however, indicate: First, that particularly during the early days of the districts, county governing bodies were inclined to view the district's operation as a *government* program for which no strain on local financial resources was necessary. Second, counties in New York and Wisconsin, where the district has particularly close organizational tie-ins with the county, have given more assistance to districts than have counties in other states. Third, the amount of county assistance to districts is on the increase. This trend is due to the rising influence of the supervisors associations and to the increasing popular support the districts are receiving from county farmers. Finally, in spite of the trend toward increased county assistance, county and townships are not yet making significant contributions in comparison to those of the federal government and the states.

The types of assistance which counties, in a sporadic and scattered fashion, are making available to districts are so variable that they cannot be completely listed. But the following services by the counties are most frequently obtained by the districts: First, a varying number of counties, in practically all states, provide free office space for district headquarters and/or local SCS technicians. The Service has generally pushed for such arrangements with the county, and the district supervisors have been successful in negotiating with county governing bodies for office space. Second, counties have loaned machinery to districts. Third, in several states, counties have helped to finance the purchase of district equipment. Finally, the special services of county officials, such as the highway engineer, the county auditor, and the county attorney, are commonly available to district supervisors.

State contributions to districts have been largely in the form of specific legislative appropriation.[31] These appropriations for the district program have been steadily increasing. State legislatures have made the following total sums available: In the year 1944, $823,471; in 1945, $1,067,221; in 1946, $2,026,597; in 1947, $2,755,561, and in 1951, $10,029,121. State appropriations available for the district program, in 1951, ranged from $475 in Wyoming to $5,270,056 in Texas. In that year, five states had appropriations in excess of $500,000 each and nine states in excess of $100,000.[32]

The above figures are somewhat misleading, because some of the state appropriations are on a one-year basis and others are on a two-year basis. Also, they include revolving funds, as in Texas and California. As J. C. Dykes, Assistant Chief of SCS, explained it:

... if we take out of the $10 million total those appropriations that are made to permanent revolving funds, for example the one in Texas for $5 million and the $1 million appropriation in California, and put it on a current expenditure basis, I think districts have about $2 million in State funds currently available. If you add to that all that has been done in the way of setting up revolving funds the total is much higher. With revolving funds districts buy equipment, the States recover the cost of that equipment as the districts rent it to farmers and deposit rental fees in the State treasury, then the money is loaned to other districts to buy equipment. Since these funds revolve and they

---

[31] See table on state appropriations in House Appropriation Hearings, 1952 (Part 2), op. cit., p. 795.
[32] Texas, $5,270,056; California, $1,032,427; Louisiana, $750,000; Iowa, $570,000; Kentucky, $536,000; Oklahoma, $368,280; Pennsylvania, $200,000; Virginia, $152,000; and Washington, $150,000.

are spent over and over again, a new equipment appropriation is not required annually in the States having revolving funds.[33]

Even so, when allowances are made for the revolving funds, state appropriations available in 1951 were still some 300 per cent larger than in 1947.

State appropriations generally are made to the state soil conservation committee[34] for two large purposes — state committee expenses and direct assistance to districts. Districts use their allotments for a variety of purposes such as:

1. Travel and expenses for members of district governing bodies while on official duties, including attendance at regular or called meetings.
2. Clerical, space, printing, mailing and other office expense.
3. Acquire, operate and maintain equipment, also services of contractors.
4. Field assistants necessary to operate and maintain field equipment.
5. Part- or full-time work-manager for the district governing body.
6. Planting materials for use on critical areas.
7. Workers to help landowners and operators with application and maintenance of conservation practices and land use.[35]

Of the total state appropriations of $10,029,121, only $676,331 is allocated for expenses of state committees. The remaining $9,352,790 is allocated for the direct assistance to districts. Again the range in that part of state appropriations which is directly allotted to the districts is wide. Twelve states, in 1951, allocated no funds for directly assisting districts.[36] On the other hand, six states each allocated for their districts sums which totaled in excess of $300,000.[37]

In addition to the state funds directly appropriated for the district program, state agencies also give the districts material assistance of various kinds. Of course, the assistance of the state Extension Services is so intimate a part of the workings of the district that it need not even be mentioned here. No reliable basis has yet been developed for reporting and evaluating the assistance afforded districts by forestry departments, highway departments, wildlife commissions and so on.

If the district has proved a good device for securing state con-

---

[33] House Appropriation *Hearings*, 1952 (Part 2), *op. cit.*, p. 796.
[34] In some states called commission, commissioners, board, or division.
[35] House Appropriation *Hearings*, 1952 (Part 2), *op. cit.*, p. 795.
[36] Arizona, Colorado, Florida, Illinois, Indiana, Kansas, Mississippi, Nebraska, New York, Ohio, Wisconsin, Wyoming.
[37] Texas, $5,148,845; California, $1,000,000; Louisiana, $750,000; Kentucky, $522,000; Iowa, $500,000; and Oklahoma $364,230.

servation assistance, the bulk of the credit must go to the district supervisors. These leading and influential farmers have not hesitated to press their states' legislators and administrative chiefs for district aid. Commonly, supervisors work through their state association to impress legislators with the need for conservation appropriations. Also, they seek to accomplish their purpose indirectly through the state soil conservation committee. The steady increase in total state appropriations since 1944 is not unrelated to the fact that supervisors' associations have during this same period been increasing in number, membership, and aggressiveness.

Although there is no reason to assume that the present trend toward increased state contributions has reached its peak, there is still small likelihood that state contributions will approach those made by the federal government. Nevertheless, to the district device must go the large share of credit for whatever those state contributions have been or may be. As legal creatures of the state, administratively manned by important farm people, the districts are able to obtain more state assistance for public conservation activity than could likely be had through any direct federal program.

INFLUENCE OF DISTRICT UPON NATIONAL PROGRAM

District effectiveness in achieving conservation does not depend alone upon the amount of resources thrown into the program. As already pointed out, it also depends upon making wise use of such resources. Effective utilization of resources, in turn, depends upon district ability to winnow out the best thinking on conservation techniques and administrative practices of each of the groups participating in the district's program. District capacity to select only the best thinking from each group derives largely from its ability to strike a productive balance between national programming and local determination.

To appraise the potentialities of the district, as a device for developing a constructive synthesis of national, state, and local thought, it is necessary to analyze the functioning of the district in terms of (1) the effect the district has thus far had upon the national SCS conservation program during its fifteen years of operation; and (2) factors in district conservation administration which might be expected to influence the district's future course as a government unit.

It is commonly predicted that the district as it gains in maturity —in terms of its reliance upon its own resources for equipment and conservation materiel, its supervisor government's developing an active competence, and its growing outside counter-balancing supports — may have a strong impact upon the national conservation program. But, young as the district still is, it already has been responsible for bringing about modifications in the over-all national program. On a daily operating basis, it has been making local adjustments in the national pattern to suit local circumstances.

It does not follow, however, that these modifications have always come about because of the strength and aggressiveness of local boards in managing their district's affairs. The district's status as a legal unit of local government, with an independent local governing body responsible only to the farmers of the district, has enabled local SCS employees to take effective stands for the local adjustments they believe necessary. The technician can form a common local front with the supervisors.

Without the support of the independent district governing bodies, the Service's district technicians — despite the fact that they are in position to see how Service administrative directives are working out locally — would probably have little voice in the Service's determination of necessary technical standards and adequate administratvie processes. The presence of the district governing bodies has meant that technicians, seeing the faults in particular national directives, can speak to the higher adminis-trative levels through the voice of their governing boards.

This does not mean that supervisor reactions to SCS sugges-tions on how to administer their districts are not often controlling in technician-supervisor relations. In the first place, the local technicians, in their close associations with the supervisors, are sensitive to supervisor reactions. For example, local technicians react against the red tape in Service-district and district-farmer relationships because they find themselves having to justify it to scoffing supervisors and farmers. Some technicians resented the Washington office's putting out an informational bulletin on land-use regulations in 1947 because they feared it might upset their good relations with their supervisors. The emphasis of the state SCS office upon the technicians' maintaining harmonious working relations with governing bodies adds to their desire to get along with the supervisors.

When the technician uses the weight of the governing body

in expressing his views to higher administrative levels, he often is merely organizing and vocalizing supervisor reactions. Therefore, although it has not always been the supervisors themselves who have directly sought modifications of the national program, supervisor government surely has facilitated the bringing about of such adjustments.

The single most important area in which supervisor government has modified the national conservation program has been in the determining of the relationships and obligations of farmers to the conservation program. The Service, looking at the conservation problem in terms of the technical adequacy of control measures, has from the beginning believed in the necessity for obligating a cooperating farmer to a complete farm conservation plan. Although SCS is now, as a result of the February, 1951, reorganization, encouraging the districts to permit a farmer to become a district cooperator before he has received a farm plan, it has not retracted on the ultimate need for a complete farm plan.

Although the reorganization was the immediate cause of the setting up of the three-stage procedure for a farmer's acceptance of a farm plan,[38] the new process was in accordance with a growing SCS recognition of the practical need for reducing for farmers the obstacles to getting into the district program. Under the influence of farmer supervisor opinion, SCS has over a ten-year period been modifying its definition of what a complete farm plan entails and has been relaxing its requirements on how the complete farm plan can be brought into effect.

In the early days, the obligation of the complete farm plan was interpreted by the Service as being the complete carrying out by the farmer of all necessary practices upon his total farm. Declared Chief Bennett, in 1937:

> The excuses frequently offered — that "the farmer is not ready for a complete land use program;" that "it is inconvenient;" or that "he is not sufficiently sold on strip-cropping, contour cultivation, terracing and other necessary practices," — are not adequate from the standpoint of effective prosecution of the Service program. The answer to them is simply that a partial program for a given farm does not meet the essential requirements of a good soil conservation program and is, therefore, not acceptable. The program for each farm. . .must call for the *full* treatment of *every* acre affected and for the employment of *all*

---

[38] *See* pages 37–39.

measures and practices needed to provide that treatment. Otherwise, the Soil Conservation Service fails to discharge its full responsibility.[39]

From the beginning, district administrations have not accepted the necessity or expediency for demanding that a farmer accept a complete farm plan. Both supervisors and technicians, in their contact with their district's farmers, were convinced that letting farmers sample a few practices before requiring them to take a complete plan was the best method of selling district farmers on the value of conservation. Consequently, in the years before the war, despite Service insistence on the complete plan, the farm plan as an instrument for organizing and spreading conservation work was undergoing strain. In the first place, technicians were devoting considerable of their work time to "bootlegging" fragmentary conservation jobs to farmers. Secondly, because a farmer was required to accept all of the practices outlined in his farm plan, many technicians were writing plans which were fragmentary and incomplete.

The impracticality of requiring a complete plan was emphasized over and over through all of the upward channels of district-SCS communication. The general urgings from the district were: (1) that a farmer, in accepting a complete farm plan, should not be required to obligate himself to carry out all of the practices set forth in the plan; and/or (2) that farmers should be given assistance in carrying out single practices before they be required to sign a conservation agreement.

The war provided the Service with a graceful "out" in relaxing its requirements for a complete farm plan. Said Bennett:

Although the treatment of all the land comprising a farm is the only certain means of achieving effective soil and water conservation on that farm, still the Service would be remiss in its responsibilities if it continued to operate within pre-war limitations during the period of national emergency.[40]

Therefore, under a *widespread practices* program, inaugurated in 1942, Service technicians were permitted to assist farmers without farm plans in the application of relatively simple, production-conservation practices.[41] Despite the fact that the new program

---

[39] "Emphasizing Complete Farm Planning," SCS Field Memorandum No. 475, April 29, 1937.

[40] *Report of the Chief of the Soil Conservation Service,* 1943, p. 10.

[41] "Widespread Application," SCS Field Memorandum, No. 1078, October 14, 1942.

was popular with local technicians, supervisors, and farmers, the Service felt it necessary to cancel the wartime memorandum permitting conservation work to be done "on the widespread."[42]

Nevertheless, SCS continued in its relaxation of requirements for a complete farm plan. In the first place, the Service changed its position upon what constitutes a complete farm plan. A plan for a farm was to be considered complete if it covered the whole farm even though it did not obligate a farmer to carry out all of the practices set forth. That is, the farm plan was to be written in two parts. The first part listed the *agreed upon* practices. The second part listed the *recommended practices*, with no compulsion upon the agreeing parties to carry them out.

This innovation was an important compromise between advocates of the complete farm plan or nothing, and proponents of the carrying out of as many conservation practices as possible regardless of the presence of a farm plan. Under the new procedure, many farmers could be brought into official cooperation with the district on the basis of committing themselves only to a few practices. It was soon officially discovered that farmers, accepting a part of the plan, were seeing the advantages of going on and completing additional practices.

In another respect, also, the Service found it necessary to modify the obligations it has expected the farmer to assume. At least partly because of the reactions of supervisors to the attitudes of farmers in their districts,[43] the farm conservation plans have become increasingly practical from the standpoint of the farmer's making a living from his farm. That is, the Service is not asking a farmer to accept a plan which SCS believes does not fit his business as well as the conservation needs of his land.

Although from the standpoint of erosion control, the use and treatment of a given area of land should be determined by its physical characteristics, the Service, partly because of district reactions, now instructs its local technicans to weigh such considerations as available facilities, implements, power, labor, financial means, preference of the farmer, his ability to learn, his willingness to try new methods, and above all, his economic ability to shift from cash income crops.[44]

---

[42] SCS Field Memorandum, No. 1023E, April 15, 1947.

[43] This increased consideration of the business problems of the farmer by SCS may also have been prompted by Extension and Farm Bureau criticism of the impracticability of the farm conservation plan, as well as by SCS's own experience in the writing and application of plans.

[44] *Report of the Chief of the Soil Conservation Service*, 1946, p. 11.

As early as 1948, serious thought was given by the Washington office to the development of an official national procedure which would permit technicians to give preliminary assistance to farmers without a plan. Under this procedure, the farm planners, with the approval of the supervisors, could render limited technical service to farmers who had made application for a farm plan, but who had not yet been able to get a plan prepared. The work, the proposed memorandum specified, must be of such a nature that it could be included in the plan when it was later drawn up. Although this proposal was not adopted, it is in essence the new three-stage procedure which went into effect in April, 1951.

The various regional offices have in recent years been sanctioning procedures whose chief purpose was to permit SCS technicians to render assistance to farmers who had not yet accepted a farm plan. For example, Region IV developed what it called a progressive conservation plan in which the planning of a farm could take place over a period of from one to three years. The Region IV office explained:

If we will gear our organization to give technical assistance progressively as the farmers gain in knowledge and experience, we will eliminate a lot of time now being spent attempting to sell or educate the farmer in the beginning on a coordinated conservation program. . . . Farmers are going to apply and maintain a coordinated conservation program only as rapidly as they gain experience and we are able to give necessary technical assistance, regardless of whether or not we spend a lot of time attempting to sell them on the coordinated program in the beginning.[45]

In effect, such progressive planning was little more than a systematization of fragmentary planning, although the declared intent of the farmer was perhaps different. Region III has long given official recognition to what it calls the pre-planning activities of Service technicians.

Although it was the outside force of the Secretary's 1951 reorganization order which finally prompted the Service officially to relax its requirement of a farm plan as a prerequisite to a farmer's signing a district agreement and receiving technical assistance, the new procedure is, in fact, the inevitable outcome of the prevailing trend in SCS and district thought.

Although SCS relaxation of its requirements on the complete farm plan was a victory for district opinion, curiously enough,

---

[45] "Progressive Conservation Planning," Project Plans Division, SCS Region IV, Memorandum, August 2, 1946.

district administration in the future may become a force for the retention and strengthening of the complete plan as the chief instrumentality in the accomplishment of the federal conservation program. In the dynamics of SCS-district relationships a curious phenomenon in national-local governmental relations has been unfolding. Whereas during the first years of the district's existence, its local discretion was circumscribed by federal insistence that the district be bound to a high level of conservation performance, today the district feels its strength threatened by federal relaxation of these same requirements upon the district.

Built upon the concept of a complete and balanced conservation program for the entire farm, the district sees that its peculiar advantage in the coordinated federal conservation program lies in its high technical standards, its insistence on complete conservation. It sees that its strength with the farmers of a county is built on federal insistence on a farmer's developing a complete plan. Thus, district administration, through its supervisor associations, is acting as a force for getting acceptance of the complete farm plan as the basic instrument in the federal Department's entire conservation program. Secretary Brannan's April, 1952 memorandum in which he declared it to be the objective of the Department to provide every farmer with a complete plan was in direct response to supervisor pressure.[46] In short, future district influence upon the national conservation program may take the form of action to maintain and strengthen the goal of the complete farm plan.

Even more clearly defined has been the reaction of district administration to compelling a farmer to carry on conservation measures. Despite the fact that one of the chief reasons for turning to the use of a legal district rather than a voluntary association was so that conservation administration could use the police power to enforce compliance upon any recalcitrant minority of farmers, the land-use regulation has been practically ignored by the districts. Nor did the districts ever make any effort legally to enforce the farmer-district agreement, or to recover damages under the liability clause usually contained in the older type of agreement. The general feeling of supervisors was expressed by the chairman of the Coosa River District, Alabama: "You can't sell a man anything if he thinks you might try to make him do it." So general are the provisions of the agreements which are being adopted to conform with the new procedure for accepting a farm

---

[46] Memorandum from Secretary C. F. Brannan to G. F. Geissler, Administrator, PMA, and R. M. Salter, Chief, SCS, April 9, 1952.

plan that the question of enforcement and liability will not likely arise.

The simplification and shortening of the formal documents for organizing the relationships between the Service, district, and farmer has been another area in which the district has influenced federal policies. The trend toward the shortening and simplification of the farm plan probably has been most noticeable. In the early days of the district, farm plans were voluminous, complicated, and highly technical in language. The goal seemingly was to make the plans as learned and mysterious as possible. Large batches of mimeographed technical material were thrown in for good measure. The farm plan, in the early days, was a technician's plan rather than a plan a farmer could easily use as a guide in his conservation work.

So widespread was the reaction of supervisors and farmers against such technical plans that every region has in recent years been guiding and urging its technicians to prepare brief, to-the-point plans which are easily understandable to farmers. One region in its attempt to abbreviate the farm plan simplified it to such an extent that it may have defeated the purpose of making the plan a guide for farmers. The Region I office was probably criticizing its sister region's procedure when it explained in a memorandum to its field staff:

A sketchy outline of what kind of work is to be done on the farm is not sufficient to constitute a well-prepared plan. Instances of statements, such as "manage," . . . "consult your county agent for further assistance on pasture and hay land treatment," "construct outlet channel" and similar statements are poor advice if they stop there. They provide a poor record of understanding with the cooperator. If the woodland is to be managed, the recommendations should be in the farm plan. If certain seeding recommendations are needed, the recommendations should be included. It has been brought to light in a number of cases that aids have had difficulty in helping the farmer establish practices due to the lack of sufficient detail in the plans.[47]

Simultaneously with the shortening and simplification of the farm plan has been a briefing down of the farmer-district agreement to essential points in respective obligations. The abbreviated forms which districts throughout the country are now adopting are in line with this trend. District programs and work plans have also been shortened and simplified and put in the language of the farmers. The earlier district programs not infrequently ran from

_____
[47] Memorandum from O. C. Bruce, Chief of Operations, SCS Region I, to State and District Conservationists, September 27, 1946.

100 to 150 pages. Now they generally range from four to forty pages. In the last few years, with the sanction of the Washington office, newly created districts have been combining their programs and work plans into a single short document.

Along with supervisor reactions against long and formal documents and instruments of agreement has been a disinclination actually to use such organizing instruments. The practicality of spending time developing the program and work plan has commonly been questioned because of the fact that these documents are in general disuse in the districts. Nor have supervisors generally seen any good coming out of making a farmer sign an agreement with the district, when the nature of the district program is so highly voluntary. Thus far, however, the Service has not been willing to abandon any of the organizational documents. But it may be that they will gradually be sloughed off by district administration. In its increased tendency to make outright grants of equipment to districts, perhaps the Service already has responded to district disinclination to fool with red tape — thus eliminating the formal accountings involved in the loan of SCS equipment.

Another way in which the practical thinking of farmer administration has been influencing the national program is in the greater concern SCS has shown in balancing conservation application with planning. Although the number of farmer-district agreements in existence may "ring the cash register" in getting public appropriations, supervisor administration sees the true return in getting conservation practices onto the lands of the district. Under the 1951 arrangement for integrating SCS technical work with the PMA conservation payment program, the supervisors may find their role reversed. Their problem may well become one of preventing application from surging ahead of planning. They may feel it necessary to protect SCS technicians from pressures to apply practices without consideration for their being a complementary part of a total farm plan.

CHAPTER 7

Future of the Soil Conservation Districts

The soil conservation district is a flourishing, going concern that has an important spot in the rural government of America. Within the next few years almost all of rural United States will be covered into soil conservation districts. But there still remain these large questions: What will the soil conservation districts of the future be like? Will they become mere local outlets for the conservation program of a national agency, or will they continue to grow in local independence and strength? How will they be geared in with the total conservation job for which the national government is responsible? What are the most promising potentialities of the district, and what are its limitations?

No single answer to these questions can be given. The course the district will take in its development as a governmental unit will depend in part upon the nature of the conservation job ahead. What the district's program of action will be is dependent upon the interplay of such factors as the physical and economic needs of conservation and the pull and tug of the political and institutional forces at work in conservation. The effectiveness of the soil conservation district will depend upon how well its program is adapted to conservation needs and, in turn, upon how well its organization and working process fits its program of action.

NATURE OF FUTURE CONSERVATION PROGRAM

The nature of the program which will be required to meet society's conservation goals in the future will be largely determined by the economic environment in which the conservation work is to be carried on. It might be added that the conservation goals society sets will themselves be influenced by the economic environment.

Effect of Economic Environment

The real needs of a conservation program operating in a shrinking economy of declining markets, agricultural surplus, and low farm prices will be quite different from those of a program during a period of high industrial activity and relatively scarce farm commodities. According to economic theory, there is little need for public subsidization of the conservation practices of commercial farmers during a period of generally high farm prices. Indeed, if demand outruns supply, the chief task of government may be to act as a brake against the pressure for new exploitations of the soil.

A depression economy would create an entirely different set of requirements for an effective conservation program. The problem then would be to gear conservation to a program for adjusting production downward to estimated national needs. In early 1950, the chief of the Soil Conservation Service foresaw a period when farm supplies would overbalance demand. In his 1949 annual report, he pointed out the need for relating possible future curtailments in production to the establishment of suitable conservation practices:

> If, actually, we are entering a period when the production of some of our agricultural products will exceed the demand, it is highly important that any adjustments in production be made on the soundest possible basis. . . . Whenever it becomes necessary to make any downward adjustments in the acreage planted to our soil-depleting crops, it would be much better to make the adjustments on the basis of the capability of the land, rather than on the basis of the historical use of the land.[1]

Federal subsidy may be essential for depression land-use adjustment. Not only must a farmer be compensated for his voluntary relinquishment of a part of his share of a shrinking farm income, but his depression income probably would not permit him to make the outlays necessary for carrying out major conservation practices. Moreover, depression may again create reservoirs of unemployed labor which could be mobilized in rural works projects, one of the most rewarding of which is soil conservation.

Other Factors Influencing Program

Even without depression conditions, the total conservation program of the future likely will not be the simple, direct physical-biological undertaking that the Soil Conservation Service usu-

---

[1] *Report of the Chief of the Soil Conservation Service,* 1949, pp. 2, 3.

ally seems to envisage. As the conservation job goes forward and as the agricultural area untreated by conservation practices narrows down, the tasks of establishing conservation will become progressively more difficult. For it has generally been the commercial farmers, the more progressive farmers, who have undertaken conservation work. The marginal farmer, the subsistence farmer, and the tenant, whose lands are often most heavily eroded and whose soil fertility is most heavily mined, are frequently least economically capable of farming each acre according to its capability and of providing equipment and materiel for carrying out conservation work.

Thus, as the program narrows down to the marginal farming group, it can be anticipated that conservation will require a subsidy program adapted to the needs of its changing clientele. The conservation program of the future, if it is to achieve its ends, must come to grips with the underlying institutional obstacles to conservation: land tenure arrangements, availability of credit, and so on.

Other forces besides economic needs also help to determine the nature of a public program. However slight the economic justification for the financial subsidization of the conservation practices of commercial farmers during a period of high farm prices, the agricultural conservation payment is firmly entrenched in the federal conservation program. Political and bureaucratic pressures probably will not permit its abandonment. Any speculation upon future governmental arrangements for the achievement of conservation must be based upon the probability of the federal government's continuing to invest large public funds in conservation payments.

Therefore, whatever the economic environment may be, the withering away of the federal government in conservation cannot be anticipated. The nature of the conservation program will be such that the federal government must have a large responsibility for its effective administration. Where will the local soil conservation district fit into this larger over-all conservation undertaking? What will the nature of its program be? How will its program be geared into the over-all program? How will its organization and working process be adjusted to fit its possible future program?

Within the framework of probabilities in federal conservation programming, the course of the district as a governmental unit likely will be determined through the interplay of two forces: (1)

the real need for the development of a process which can integrate the agricultural conservation activities of federal, state, and local governments in the counties; and (2) the political, institutional, and bureaucratic drives to control the conservation program.

EFFORTS TO INTEGRATE CONSERVATION ACTIVITIES

Since the early New Deal days in agriculture — when federal action agencies began piling up in a variety of patterns — individuals, groups, agencies, and institutions with a concern in agriculture have sought a scheme for integrating the variety of federal and state programs as they come down to the farmer. Because of the pivotal relationship of conservation to all of the other agricultural problems, the coordination of conservation activity has been a central factor in each of the various plans which have been developed over the past fifteen years for rationalizing agricultural administration.

The question has been: What means can be developed for assuring that all government conservation activities are directed toward the same end, farm by farm? Two main types of solutions have been proposed. The first series of solutions proposes using the state colleges as the chief instruments in obtaining unified public conservation activity. The second group of proposals is based on the premise that the federal administration must continue to be chiefly responsible for the carrying out of the national conservation program.

Proposals for State-County Axis
LAND-GRANT COLLEGE ASSOCIATION

Proposals for integrating agricultural activity on a state-county axis recognize the federal government's right to work directly with the individual farmer only in crisis situations. The Association of Land-Grant Colleges and Universities, in 1948, warned Congress ". . . to beware of a philosophy of permanent crisis which calls for a permanent line of federal authority from Washington to the individual farm, factory, or school." [2] Those advocating the return to the traditional pattern of federal-state relationships have been particularly anxious that the conservation job be made the chief responsibility of the states. Their proposals have been based upon the premise that conservation is primarily a job in education and that the state colleges are best equipped in experience, personnel,

---

[2] U. S. Congress. House Committee on Agriculture. *Hearings on Long-Range Agricultural Policy,* Part 14, 80th Cong., 2nd Sess., 1948, p. 1549.

and administrative machinery and procedures for carrying educational programs to the counties.

The core of Extension education, according to the testimony of the Land-Grant College Association, is that of diffusing practical information about farm and home practices, and securing their adoption by means of field demonstrations and publications. However, such activities are interpreted to include the carrying of a variety of personal services to the farmers. Among these are assisting in the establishment of soil conservation districts, and through advice and counsel working very closely with the soil conservation supervisors.[3]

The Land-Grant College committee claims that the program of the Soil Conservation Service has worked itself over into the domain of the Extension Service — personal service and education:

With the passing of the camps [CCC], the grants-in-aid were gradually diminished and more and more emphasis laid upon personal technical service in laying out farm plans, assisting in many ways the soil conservation districts — which we now have by the hundreds — and increasingly upon education and demonstration.

The present situation, then, is that there are in each State two agencies carrying on educational work in soil conservation. One is the State agricultural-extension service, with a long history of work in this field, financed by funds from the State and from grants-in-aid from the Congress. The other, the Soil Conservation Service, is supported entirely by Federal funds. However, the job to be done has been a tremendous one, and in most States various techniques of cooperation between the agencies have been worked out. But the fact remains that there exist side by side in every State two independent agencies both supported in whole or in part by funds from the Federal Treasury with partially duplicating soil conservation programs, due to shifting of emphasis on the part of the Federal service increasingly to programs which are essentially educational.[4]

Therefore, the Association urged Congress carefully to study the wisdom of this duplication of agencies. Its solution for the overlapping in the work of the conservation agencies was to turn the federal conservation programs over to the states to administer:

The land-grant colleges and universities, through their experiment stations and extension services, should conduct the educational and demonstrational program as they clearly are authorized to do by State and Federal law and by long-standing agreement. Those phases of the program which are strictly "action" in character should be conduct-

---

[3] *Ibid.*, pp. 1551, 1552.
[4] *Ibid.*, p. 1552.

ed by other State agencies, such as the State soil conservation committee set up under State law in all the States. There should be close relationship between those charged with the educational and action phases of the program.

We believe that overlapping and duplication of activity at the State and county level will largely disappear if educational and action programs are made definite State responsibilities with the functions of the agencies conducting them clearly defined.[5]

According to the Land-Grant College proposals, a special state agency would largely take over the action activities of both SCS and the ACP program. In other words, the work of SCS and ACP branch of PMA would, in the words of John D. Black: " . . . be carved up into 48 separate state jurisdictions." Black speculates further on the meaning of the Land-Grant College proposal:

The federal office of the SCS might be abolished altogether, but probably would be continued with advisory and promotion functions to perform more or less like the present federal Office of Education. The federal office of the PMA would surely be continued, and would function much like the present federal Bureau of Public Roads. Presumably these state committees would administer any program of payment for practices, and likewise any marketing quotas that might be voted. By implication, even "the furnishing of credit facilities," since this is included in the list of actions, if it is subsidized in any way, would be turned over to the states to be administered in this way.[6]

AMERICAN FARM BUREAU FEDERATION

The American Farm Bureau Federation has long concerned itself with the problem of the overlapping, duplication, and conflict of effort within the Department of Agriculture. In the spring of 1943, it urged Congress to transfer to the state and county Extension Services all educational, informational, and promotional work of the action programs and the service work of the Farm Security Administration. Since 1947, the Farm Bureau has been concentrating on a campaign for the decentralization and coordination of agricultural conservation programs by making federal funds available for agricultural conservation to the states on a grant-in-aid basis.

LEGISLATIVE PROPOSALS

One of the first legislative proposals for implementing a state-local axis in conservation was the Hill-Cooley Bill, introduced in

[5] *Ibid.*, pp. 1552, 1553.

[6] John D. Black, "Federal-State-Local Relations in Agriculture," mimeographed by National Planning Association, January 7, 1949, p. 30.

July, 1947.[7] Although its stated purpose was to avoid duplication and conflicts in agricultural soil and water conservation programs, it did not propose the consolidation of the ACP and SCS programs. Rather it proposed to achieve coordination by transferring the administration of SCS at the national level to the federal Extension Service. At the state level, SCS's educational, demonstrational and technical services were to be transferred to the state Extension Services. Its research was to become the concern of the state Agricultural Experiment Stations. The name "SCS" was to apply to a division of the Extension Service. The regional offices of SCS were to be abolished.

The Aiken Bill, of March, 1948, represented one of the strongest efforts to integrate soil conservation activities on a state basis.[8] It too proposed decentralizing conservation administration to state and county units. The ACP and SCS program functions were to be performed at the state and county levels insofar as the Secretary deemed practicable, by state agricultural councils and county agricultural associations, whose executive committees would carry out the actual administration of the state and county programs. The State Agricultural Council was to be composed of an ex-officio state college group and the state Commissioner of Agriculture, plus elected farmer committeemen. It was to employ a state administrator.

The county agricultural association or county agricultural program committee was to be composed of elected farmer members, plus an ex-officio group consisting mainly of the governing body of the soil conservation district, plus the county Extension agent. It was definitely provided, however, that the district supervisors were to be in a minority on the county committee. Most of the federal employees in the action programs would become the professional employees of the state and county councils. The soil conservation district supervisors were to be a minority on a county committee which was to develop and administer the county agricultural program. The state soil conservation committee was not to be represented as such on the State Agricultural Council.

Again in 1951, Senator Aiken introduced a bill, sponsored by the Citizens Committee for the Hoover Report, which the district supervisors' associations interpreted as an attempt to deliver the

---

[7] H. R. 4151, 80th Cong., 1st Sess.
[8] S. 2318, 80th Cong., 2nd Sess.

Soil Conservation Service over to the states.[9] The bill proposed the creation within the Department of Agriculture of an Agricultural Consultation Service, which would be made up of the federal Extension Service, the agencies carrying on the Smith-Hughes vocational agriculture work, and the Soil Conservation Service. This was seen as an effort to implement the argument that the program of technical on-site assistance provided farmers by SCS was not an "action" activity, but a program of advice, consultation and education, which belonged in the domain of the state colleges. The district supervisor associations termed this a "clear attempt to renew the provisions of the Reed-Cooley-Hill bill."

At the same time, the conservation payment program of the PMA was to be transferred to an Agricultural Resources Conservation Service. At the state and county levels, the new conservation service was to receive "advice" from state and county advisory agricultural councils created under the bill. The county agricultural councils were to be composed of five elected farmer committeemen. Seven members of the state council were to be farmers elected from the county councils. The remaining six individuals on the state council were to be ex-officio members from state agricultural agencies. Apparently, the payment leg of the federal conservation program, under the provisions of the bill, would again be administered without benefit of substantial technical assistance. Moreover, the need for bringing about an horizontal coordination at the federal level of the conservation payment program and the program for giving on-site technical assistance was overlooked. Even on the local level, there was no provision for either the Agricultural Consultation Service or the local soil conservation district to advise or assist in the conservation payment program.

TASK FORCE OF HOOVER COMMISSION

One of the major concerns of the Agricultural Task Force of the Hoover Commission, under the chairmanship of Dean H. P. Rusk of the University of Illinois, was to eliminate the duplication and conflict in conservation activities. Like the Land-Grant College Association, the Farm Bureau Federation, and the sponsors of the Hill-Cooley and the Aiken Bills, the Task Force proposed to eliminate duplication in conservation by assigning the responsibility for conservation administration to

---

[9] S.1149, 82nd Cong., 1st Sess.

the state Extension Services. It believed that its recommendation would do away with the conflict between, and the overlapping activities of, the Extension Service and the Soil Conservation Service. This the Task Force felt would eliminate questions of jurisdictions and responsibility that lead to situations in which employees of each were known to try to make separate conservation plans for the same farm.[10]

Believing that the technical assistance given farmers through the Soil Conservation Service was largely educational and demonstrational in nature, it proposed that federal technical assistance be made available through the Extension Administration of the United States Department of Agriculture and the Extension Services of the respective states to the soil-conservation districts and other organizations and farmers. The truncated Soil Conservation Service, the Soil and Water Conservation Service of the proposed new Agricultural Resources Conservation Administration, was to have the responsibility of coordinating through planning the soil conservation work on a regional basis and of integrating state programs with a national conservation plan.[11] The SCS field technicians would disappear. In their stead, the state Extension Services with federal funds would employ conservation specialists who would aid the farmer in his conservation work.

Under the Task Force proposals, the soil conservation districts would seemingly have continued in their same operational pattern, except that the state Extension Services, rather than SCS, would furnish them technical assistance. The farm plan — or at least the complete conservation treatment of the farm — was to be the basis for the extension of governmental assistance. Conservation payments to a farmer were to be restricted to those which brought about the adoption of complete and balanced soil-conservation programs on his farm, and were not to be used as income supplements in disguise. When the conservation plan on any farm was completed, payments to the owner were to stop.[12]

Although the forces which have sought to achieve the integration of the various conservation activities on a state-county axis have been powerful, the Department of Agriculture, supported by the farmer clientele of PMA and SCS, has been strong

[10] Task Force Report on *Agricultural Activities,* January, 1949, p. 78.
[11] *Ibid.,* p. 37.
[12] *Ibid.,* p. xvi.

enough to block all Congressional moves to turn the federal conservation programs over to the states. In recent legislative sessions, it has been possible to compromise on the content of the national agricultural policy. But no agreement could be reached on vertical inter-agency relationships except to stay with the *status quo*. Therefore, at least in the foreseeable future, the role of the district as a governmental unit will not be modified because of state assumption of the national conservation programs.

A shift in conservation administration from a federal to a state basis should not in and of itself significantly affect the position of the district in the total conservation program. Because the Soil Conservation Service has always stood in the position of the districts' protector and defender and has nurtured their growth in number and strength, it can be convincingly argued that any move to eliminate SCS as a national agency would threaten the district's position in the conservation movement. The district might be forced to go it alone. This is not necessarily true, however. The districts have been building up powerful support within the states, which should make a state agency amenable to working through the district.

The crux of the various proposals, from the district's standpoint, is the role that is assigned the districts in the total national-state program. There are three levels of possibilities for the district's role in the total conservation program: (1) The district might be made the local unit through which all federal and state conservation assistance is channeled to farmers. (2) The district could be a major member of a more inclusive county committee, responsible for developing an over-all conservation or even total agricultural program for the county. (3) The district could be by-passed and isolated from the main stream of federal and state assistance to the farmer. In part, at least, the key to what the position of the district can be in local conservation activity lies in top-level acceptance of the concept of the complete farm plan — or at least of what the farm plan has come to symbolize — farmer acceptance and carrying through of a technically adequate combination of conservation practices.

Coordination on Federal-County Axis

The second series of efforts to develop an integrated agricultural administration have been based upon the assumption that the federal government must continue to be chiefly responsible for the administration of the national conservation programs. Consequently, the advocates of integrating agricultural activities on a federal-county axis have been largely preoccupied with the effort to develop administrative arrangements for coordinating the activities of the federal action agencies in agriculture. Their plans too have been rooted in the belief that coordination also is to be achieved through local participation in the development of county policy.

OFFICE OF LAND-USE COORDINATION

The first effort of the Department of Agriculture to pull its mushrooming assortment of activities into a unified program centered around the use of the land. The Office of Land-Use Coordination, set up in Secretary Wallace's office under Milton Eisenhower in 1937, was originally designed to achieve an overall coordination of the activities of the Department concerned with land use. After the establishment of the State and County Land-Use Planning Program, in 1938, however, the Office became chiefly occupied in coordinating flood control activities, the Water Facilities program, the Wheeler-Case small irrigation projects, and so on. The Office of Land-Use Coordination has little significance in the district movement, except that it shows how early the Department was aware of the need for bringing its various land activities into an harmonious program.

STATE AND COUNTY LAND-USE PLANNING

The State and County Land-Use Planning Program, established by the federal department and the Land-Grant Colleges in the fall of 1938, was an effort to achieve both vertical and horizontal integration of the agricultural activities of federal, state and local governments. Through cooperative planning at community, county and state levels — by committees composed of farmers and representatives of all agricultural agencies — county and state programs and plans were to flow upwards to Washington. Here they were to be used as a basis for adjusting national programs to local circumstances and for coordinating the work of the various agencies. They were to be processed by the Bureau of Agricultural Economics and special interdepartmental coordinating committees, and finally acted upon by a top level Program Board, composed of the heads of the various bureaus and agencies.

A cooperative process, rather than agency consolidation, was to be the means of achieving coordination of federal agency activities and also a gearing together of national, state, and local programs. Although the state colleges were not to take over the administration of federal programs, they were to have a significant part in the development of their policies. One of the chief causes of the failure of Land-Use Planning was its inability to get the real cooperation of the powerful federal action agencies. Although the AAA was the least cooperative of all the agencies, the Soil Conservation Service did not see the real need for gearing the districts into such an over-all process. In some regions, particularly, it was believed that farmers could do all of their land-use planning through their districts.

Failing to get the cooperation of the action agencies and of many of the Land-Grant Colleges and receiving insufficient support from the Secretary, the Land-Use Planning process was so ineffective that it was an easy prey to the political pressures which had built up against it. Congress, in 1942, wrote an end to the Land-Use Planning experiment.

DISTRICT AS LOCAL COORDINATOR

The soil conservation district itself also has been considered as a possible mechanism for coordinating agricultural programs at the county level. In its early days the district was at least occasionally viewed by the Secretary's office as a potential local work unit for all of the departmental land-use and related programs. Secretary Wallace, in December 1937, officially expressed this view of the district:

> I hope that other agencies of the Department also will begin to move so that they may be able to work through the soil conservation districts. It seems to me that these districts in the future may be found to present an opportunity to the Department to unify a number of the different action programs which the Department is now authorized to carry on. Through the local soil conservation districts the Department should be able to assist farmers in formulating and executing comprehensive plans for bringing about wise land use. I think it is important, therefore, that the districts should not come to be looked upon as having significance only for the program of the Soil Conservation Service, but that they should be seen as local governmental units, organized democratically, functioning over properly bounded areas, and possessing the necessary governmental power to enable them to carry on well-rounded agricultural programs. The districts need the help of most of the agencies of the Department and, in turn, they

can help the Department as a whole to carry out more effectively the various programs it is administering.[13]

The district has been equipped, in legal and administrative terms, to act as a channel for any agricultural agency in the land-use field which desires to utilize it. As pointed out to the action agencies by Secretary Wickard, in 1940:

> The State soil conservation districts laws have equipped the districts with the broad range of governmental powers they need to exercise in order to perform their functions well. . . . While the districts are limited to working in the field of erosion control and soil conservation that field is an enormously broad one in agriculture. In the last analysis, soil conservation can be effectively achieved only if all lands are put to their proper use. In general, the districts are authorized to do whatever is essential to achieve that objective.[14]

In revising the form for the memoranda of understanding with the individual districts in 1940, the Department attempted to develop a procedure which would permit the eventual participation of all federal agricultural agencies in assistance to districts. Under the revised procedure, the Department, rather than SCS, executes with the district a basic memorandum of understanding, which establishes the general basis for cooperation. "Subsequently, each agency of the Department that is prepared to cooperate with the particular district will enter into a supplemental memorandum of understanding or other appropriate arrangement with that district which will set forth the assistance to be made available."[15]

That the agencies might be currently informed on the areas which were coming into conservation districts, Secretary Wickard pointed out that SCS was:

> . . . issuing, and will continue to issue, periodically a statement summarizing the available information with reference to the number, location, and stage of organization of soil conservation districts throughout the country. The Service will supply copies of the statement to the Washington, regional, and State offices of the Agricultural Adjustment Administration, the Forest Service, the Farm Security Administration, Office of Land Use Coordination, and to any other agency

---

[13] Memorandum, Secretary H. A. Wallace to Chief of Soil Conservation Service, H. H. Bennett, December 10, 1937, quoted in Memorandum No. 3093, Office of Secretary, October 29, 1938.

[14] "A Statement by the Secretary of Agriculture Concerning Departmental Cooperation with Soil Conservation Districts," *op. cit.,* p. cont'd.

[15] *Ibid.,* p. cont'd. 2.

of the Department that will indicate a desire to receive this information by written request to the Service.[16]

Furthermore, district administration has attempted to develop coordinating devices and working processes which facilitate all agencies' purposefully working together within the district's program. The district program sets forth, for all agencies to consider, the problems of the district and its large, long term goals. The district work plan outlines a working process which each agency can examine to adjudge its adequacy as a basis for cooperation with the district. "The district work plan," explains the SCS, "is a presentation, at any one time, of the proposed conservation practices and methods of effectuating their application upon lands within the district, the current plan of district activities and procdures for carrying on such activities, and who, if any individual or agency, will assist the district in such activities. . . . It should provide a general answer at any one time, regarding district activities, as to what is to be done, and where, when, how, and by whom."[17]

Annual plans of work and calendars of activities provide a means of keeping a current record of exactly how and when the district proposes to carry on each of its activities. Even the farm plan is officially designed to guide cooperating agencies in rendering assistance to the individual farmers. The objectives, and the intermediary steps for accomplishing the objectives, are to be so set forth that any professional worker, upon reading the plan, can arrange his assistance accordingly. The land-use capabilities classification technique is to provide common standards and procedures which all professional workers can understand and use in determining land classes and in getting general understanding and agreement upon proper conservation treatments for each land class.

The district, as is generally known, has not developed into the coordinator of all agricultural land programs. The other action agencies were developing their own separate local outlets, and they looked upon the districts as an SCS, rather than a Departmental, outlet. The Farmers Home Administration has been the only federal action agency, outside of SCS, which has seen fit to utilize the district to any great extent. It concluded

---

[16] "Departmental Cooperation with Soil Conservation Districts," *op. cit.*, p. cont'd. 3.

[17] "District Program and Work Plan," *op. cit.*, p. cont'd. 4.

supplemental memoranda of understanding with a considerable number of districts — thus gearing its clients' farming practices into the district program. In the shifting of relationships and responsibilities under the new unification of the activities of SCS and ACP, many officials of the Service are looking to these administrative arrangements — which are still in force — as the means for making the district the chief unit for county conservation.

In recent years those seeking a means of integrating land-use activities on the basis of a continuing federal administration have shifted their emphasis away from the search for a *device* for coordinating agricultural activities — such as a cooperative planning process, a coordinating committee, a local district, or a top level board or coordinating office. Their efforts lately have been centered around plans for either the actual administrative consolidation of existing agencies performing related functions, or for placing these agencies under the close supervision and control of a common administrative superior. None of these proposals, however, has failed to provide local lay participation as a supplementary means of achieving coordination of agricultural activities in the counties.

USDA REORGANIZATION PROPOSAL (1947)

When the Department of Agriculture reexamined its organization in 1947, it gave considerable attention to the problem of integrating conservation activity. It proposed that integration be achieved first by consolidating in a single agency the programs of the Soil Conservation Service and the Agricultural Conservation Program of PMA. It gave county USDA committees the task of integrating agricultural activities within the county. The committees were to have specific administrative responsibilities and authority.

HOPE BILL

The chief legislative effort for integrating conservation activities along a federal-local axis was the Hope Bill, introduced in the spring of 1948.[18] It proposed that an Agricultural Resources Administration be set up within the Department. Not only were all of the soil and water resources activities of the Department of Agriculture to be included in the new agency, but the several land

---

[18] H.R. 6054, 80th Cong., 2nd Sess.

agencies of the Interior Department were to be transferred to it.

The role of the soil conservation district was to be greatly enlarged under the Hope Bill. As had been visualized by those originally creating the district device, the district was to be the local unit through which all federal conservation assistance was channeled to farmers. The bill provided that all financial or other assistance to any person with respect to lands was to be provided through the soil conservation districts in the areas where they existed. The ACP payments for practices and improvements of a permanent or semipermanent nature were to be available only to farmers living within soil conservation districts. A farmer was required to accept a farm plan before he was entitled to payment for such practices.

Under the Hope Bill, the only job left for the PMA county committees was handling ACP payments for recurring practices that would retard depletion of soil productivity, in the agricultural areas outside organized districts. As the districts spread rapidly over the entire country, the PMA committees gradually would be without a job. As in most of the other plans, an over-all county committee, a County Agricultural Programs Board, was to be set up. Unlike the county USDA committees proposed in the 1947 plan of the Department of Agriculture, these committees were to have no operating functions. They were, however, annually to develop over-all county programs.

HOOVER COMMISSION

The Hoover Commission, in 1949, on the basis of its investigations of agricultural organization, recommended that the operational functions of the Department be grouped into eight major units. The Agricultural Resources Conservation Service, as one of the major units, was to include all major soil, range, and forest conservation agencies.[19] The Hoover Commission, itself, however, did not accept its Agricultural Task Force's recommendation that technical assistance in soil conservation work be channeled to farmers through the state Extension Services.

So difficult was it to find a formula for integrating the activities of SCS and ACP, which would be reasonably acceptable to both, that President Truman in the reorganization he proposed

---

[19] Commission on Organization of the Executive Branch of the Government, *Department of Agriculture,* House Document No. 80, 81st Cong., 1st Sess., 1949, p. 11.

Fig. 13 — System of terraces in Wisconsin with grain seeded to permanent alfalfa on terrace channels and terrace ridge.

Fig. 19 — The combined effort of state and federal agencies is necessary to the realization of the district's land-use program.

to Congress for agriculture in 1950, failed to indicate what should be done to bring the conservation programs together. His proposal's defeat in the Senate may have been partially due to its neglect of this central problem.

ACP TRANSFER OF FIVE PER CENT FUNDS TO SCS

Congressional concern over the continuing separation of the conservation payment program from the program for giving farmers technical assistance in their conservation work was indicated in the experiment which Congress authorized, on its own initiative, in the 1950 agricultural appropriation act. The act provided that any county PMA committee could transfer up to five per cent of its program funds to SCS to pay for technical assistance in applying ACP practices. The money was generally to be employed to hire semi-professional conservation aids to assist district technicians in the planning and application of conservation practices. Although both agencies professed enthusiasm for the experiment, during the 1950 fiscal year, funds were transferred by PMA committees in only 97 counties.[20] During the 1951 program year only about $150,000 was transferred in 103 counties in eighteen states.

Under the impetus of the coordination of ACP and SCS activities, called for by Secretary Brannan in February, 1951, it is estimated that the transfer of five per cent of the funds will jump to $1,500,000 during the 1952 program year.

As a device for coordinating agency activities, the inter-agency transfer of funds does not meet the efficiency test. Scarcely used until the Secretary's order for coordinating the activities of the two programs came into force, it is now an unwieldy and time consuming method of getting public funds for technical assistance into the hands of the agency actually responsible for the technical quality of the federal conservation program. So hedged about by restrictions and so tied up in procedural red tape is the transfer of funds, that SCS in many counties in several states has preferred meeting its additional load of technical responsibilities by taking under its technical direction the semi-professional technical personnel that PMA itself employs. Early reports from county PMA offices indicate that in at least 441 counties the local PMA and SCS have mutually agreed that there is no need for transferring funds during the 1952 program year.[21]

If the Soil Conservation Service is to have the authority and

---

[20] Letter from T. B. Joyce, cited.
[21] House Appropriation *Hearings*, 1953, *op. cit.*, p. 1279.

responsibility for the Department's program of technical assistance to farmers, rationalized budgetary procedure calls for Congressional appropriation of public funds for employing necessary personnel being made directly to that agency. There is some indication that the 1954 budget will be set up along those lines.

DISTRICT'S ROLE IN FUTURE CONSERVATION ADMINISTRATION

Secretary Brannan's reorganization order of February, 1951, was the culmination of the general growing dissatisfaction with the efforts of the two major federal conservation programs to work out the farmer's salvation in conservation in independence of each other.[22] Since the Secretary's memorandum, speculation on the future role of the district has been rife. On the one hand, is the fear that the district might just as well close up shop: that the district has lost its function; that it no longer has any bargaining power with farmers; and that it can no longer make independent decisions. On the other hand, there is the optimism which sees the reorganization as the greatest opportunity the district has yet had for bringing an additional 5 million farmers into its program; for raising all federal conservation activity to a high level of technical adequacy; and even for becoming the real local outlet for most land-use activities.

There are roots of reality in all of these diverse speculations. For the reorganization was, in essence, a compromise. Although it has frequently been maintained that PMA has come out "top dog," the reorganization in actuality represents no clear victory for any of the competing ideas for organizing conservation.

The several recommendations for consolidating SCS and the ACP branch of PMA into a single agency were not followed. But the various land programs of the Department were given single supervision and direction through the under-secretary, to whom the heads of the various agencies working in land and water problems are administratively responsible. The reorganization follows the 1948 Aiken Bill rather than the Hope proposals in marking out the role of the district in the total federal conservation program within each county. Rather than being the county unit through which all federal land programs are to be channeled to the farmer, the district is merely to be represented on a more inclusive county committee which has the responsibilty for formu-

---

[22] Secretary's Memorandum No. 1278, *op. cit.*

lating and determining the county's soil conservation policies and programs.

However, the county committees do not have operating responsibilities, as proposed in the 1948 Aiken Bill. The county group is to meet on the call of the chairman of the county PMA committee. The state soil conservation committee, an important agent in district administration, is not specifically designated as a member of the state group which jointly formulates and determines the soil conservation policies and programs for guidance and direction of the various federal conservation agencies operating within the state. However, it is apparently proper for the state group to invite the state soil conservation committee to participate in its deliberations.

On the other hand, the Secretary specifically directs the state PMA committees to encourage the creation and development of soil conservation districts. In an April, 1952 memorandum, Secretary Brannan strengthened and made more specific his support of the use of the district in the federal soil conservation program:

Soil conservation districts play a key role in helping farmers to get well-rounded conservation systems developed and applied. I believe that it is in the national interest for every farm and every acre of farm land in the country to be in soil conservation districts. For this reason in Memorandum No. 1278 I directed the PMA State Committee and the State Conservationist of the Soil Conservation Service to jointly encourage the creation and development of soil conservation districts.

Under the 1951 reorganization, the Soil Conservation Service, at the national and state levels, and the district supervisors and SCS field technicians, at the county level, share the responsibility for developing state and county agricultural resources conservation programs which are to serve as the basis for the determination of the ACP practices and payments.

The goal SCS has long since set for itself becomes the conservation goal of the entire Department. The Departmental objective becomes ". . .the use of each acre of agricultural land within its capabilities and the treatment of each acre of agricultural land in accordance with its needs for protection and improvement." The adequacy of proposed conservation treatments and practices is to be measured in terms of this standard. In his April, 1952 memorandum, Secretary Brannan spelled out his belief in the need for developing complete farm plans in the attainment of this objective:

It is our ultimate objective that each farmer and rancher have a scientifically developed, technically sound conservation plan related specifically to the pattern of soil and water resources of the land he operates and to his aptitudes and personal resources, and that he be furnished the technical and financial assistance needed to put that plan into use on the land.

Finally, the Soil Conservation Service is made specifically responsible for all technical phases of the permanent type of soil conservation work. But in this additional SCS responsibility lies the reorganization's greatest threat to the district's strength. It is the requirement that SCS field workers render technical assistance to ACP participants, regardless of whether they are district cooperators who have committed themselves to completing a farm plan.

What the course of the district as a governmental unit will be under the new integration of federal soil conserving activities depends upon a combination of factors.

Gearing District Into Larger Conservation Program

The district's future role in the total conservation movement depends first upon its capacity for being geared into both federal and state conservation programs. Of course, how productively the district can be meshed into the larger conservation effort depends, in turn, upon the functions and responsibilities assigned to the district in it.

The district, as has already been pointed out, has sometimes been envisaged as the local work unit for the various federal agricultural action agencies. But it is doubtful whether the district is suited to such large responsibilities in so broad a program. The district has probably had too narrow an orientation toward the physical and biological aspects of land use for it to provide a suitable unit for channeling such programs as rehabilitation services to low income farmers, extension of agricultural credit, and so on. Moreover, it is faulty administrative organization to channel all Departmental programs into a county through a mechanism that is so peculiarly and intimately related to one particular agency.

Finally, there is the question of whether the district could be given sufficient federal operational direction and control to insure proper federal responsibility in the administration of production control programs and the dispensation of money subsidies. In hearings on the Hope Bill, which proposed channeling the entire federal conservation and production control programs through the district, Under-Secretary Dodd explained the Departmental objections to such comprehensive federal use of the districts:

> Soil-conservation districts are agencies or instrumentalities of State governments with powers, of course, to obtain cooperation and assistance from various sources, including the Department of Agriculture. The Department, however, could not incorporate these districts into its administrative mechanism in the degree necessary to insure the proper execution of programs for which Congress holds the Department responsible.[23]

In contrast, Mr. Dodd points out, the USDA committees (which the Department suggested in its 1947 proposals for departmental reorganization) would:

> . . . be elected by the farmers for the particular purpose of performing definite functions in the Department of Agriculture programs and thereby would become an integral part of the Federal Government's administrative machinery for that purpose. They would be subject to provisions of law laid down by the Congress and to regulations of the Department under those provisions of law. They would be representatives of the Federal Government, responsible . . . for adaptation of the Federal programs to local requirements and conditions within the framework of law which would safeguard essential national objectives. Obviously, bodies such as soil-conservation districts which are legal entities of State governments cannot fulfill all these essential requirements.[24]

Although a district's program and working process can be largely influenced by the federal agencies, the federal government could not properly exert sufficient operating control over this independent legal entity to insure the proper execution of its program responsibilities under federal law. Moreover, if it did succeed in exercising such control, the district as an independent unit of local government would be destroyed.

The district may not be a suitable instrument for the local execution of the regulatory and money programs of the Department. But it has the potentialities for playing an important role in a broad area of public land-use and conservation activity.

[23] U. S. Congress. House Committee on Agriculture. *Hearings* on H. R. 6054, 80th Cong., 2nd Sess., May 4, 1948, p. 14.

[24] *Ibid.*, p. 14.

Whether the district can be productively geared into a broadly synthesized national, regional, and state land-use and conservation program depends, in part at least, upon the state organizations and institutions which have been developing around the district. The districts in their relationships with the federal government are not acting in isolation. State Extension Services, state soil conservation committees, and state associations of district supervisors have an important part in determining how the district is to be geared into federal conservation activity. Will they constitute an obstruction between the federal government and the districts which prevents the Department from giving the districts that minimum of national guidance which is necessary in the carrying out of a nation-wide program? Or will they aid in developing joint administrative arrangements and procedures which will facilitate the development of a truly cooperative national-state-local conservation undertaking?

POSITION OF STATE EXTENSION SERVICES

From the beginning of the district program, the state Extension Services have had a strategic role in developing conservation operations in the districts. Because of their traditional prerogative to disseminate agricultural information to the farmers of their states, their well-established facilities in organization and personnel, their experiences in educational techniques, and their well-established relationships with farmers, the Department has agreed that conservation education should be the responsibility of the state Extensions. In memoranda of understanding entered into by the SCS and each of the state Extension Services, except Pennsylvania, the Extensions are given control over conservation education. According to a policy statement on Service-Extension relationships by the Chief of SCS and the Director of Federal Extension:

It is the policy of the Soil Conservation Service to recognize the State Extension Service as the primary channel through which agricultural information can be disseminated in the State and to work through it in such manner as may be agreed upon between the two services in the release of information pertinent to soil conservation within the State. . . .

These mutually cooperative policies are founded on the assumption that the Soil Conservation Service extends to the Extension Service the prerogative of clearing agrciultural information within the State, and that the Extension Service, in accepting that prerogative, agrees at the same time to share responsibility incumbent on the Soil Conservation

Service for carrying forward adequate information relative to its program.[25]

The field of information was defined by the statement to include dissemination of subject matter and administrative information through all available means of communication, including press, radio, visual materials, and official publications.

Success of the district conservation operation depends upon a vigorous educational program before the creation of the district, and also upon a continuing educational program after the district gets into movement. The Extension is to be responsible for both educational phases. Upon request of the governing body, the Extension is also to assist the district in the development of its program and work plan.

Thus, through its administrative authority in the educational program, the Extension can facilitate or obstruct the operations program of the district. It also has the support of farmer contacts in the county, developed over years of county agent activity. The county agent is often a strategic figure in the county. Through his relationships with farm leaders he can sometimes almost control the workings of any federal program that comes into his county.

The state colleges have an opportunity to influence the workings of the district through their membership on the legal state soil conservation committee. With a few exceptions,[26] the directors of the Extension Service and Experiment Stations are members of the state committees. In addition, other state agricultural agencies, such as the Commissioner of Agriculture, take up one of the positions on these three to nine man committees. In contrast, only five state districts' laws provide that the Secretary of Agriculture *shall* appoint a representative on the state committee. These states are Kansas, Maryland, Minnesota, North

---

[25] "A Policy Statement on Relationships between the Soil Conservation Service and the Extension Service," signed by M. L. Wilson and H. H. Bennett, March 29, 1940, *Soil Conservation Service Manual*, No. 13051, p. cont'd. 6.

[26] Georgia, Oklahoma, New York, and Texas have all-farmer committees. Arkansas has an all-farmer committee which is assisted by the state's Soil and Water Division. In Arizona, Connecticut, and Illinois a single administrator in a state agency has been set up in place of a collegial body. All members of the Florida committee are from the State Board of Control. Although the state college is represented on the regular state committee in Kentucky, the committee has been circumvented by the creation of a Division of Soil and Water Resources, which has been given appropriations and most of the powers ordinarily exercised by a state committee. (For citations of all state soil conservation districts' laws, see Appendix A.)

Carolina, and North Dakota. In ten other states, the committee *may* invite the Secretary to appoint a representative. These states are Colorado, Louisiana, Mississippi, Nevada, New Mexico, Oregon, South Dakota, Utah, Virginia, and Wisconsin. In three states — Louisiana, New York, and Ohio — the committees have been established in the state college. Thus, insofar as the state committees are powerful as determiners of district policies, the Extensions again are in a strategic position between the federal conservation agency and the district.

The state Extension director and the state director of the Agricultural Experiment Station are two of the three members of the state soil conservation advisory committee. According to the standard memorandum of understanding between SCS and the Extensions, this committee is:

> . . . to assist in formulating programs for all soil conservation work in the State, in coordinating the various agencies concerned with soil conservation, in locating demonstration and other projects, in encouraging the formation by farmers of soil conservation associations, and in otherwise contributing to a unified plan of action.

In most states, however, the personnel on the advisory committee is so nearly the same as that on the legal committee that advisory committees, with the exception of a few states, have become inactive.

In a growing number of states the state colleges have been given some actual administrative and operational controls over the districts. The authority which several of the states have given the state colleges in district administration generally has been in district research and demonstration activities. In Kentucky, Ohio, and Pennsylvania, districts are to carry on research only in cooperation with the Experiment Station or some other state agency. Indiana, Iowa, and New Jersey districts may carry on research and demonstrations only in cooperation with the state college. In New York and Pennsylvania, state college cooperation is necessary for the publication of plans and information by the districts.

The state colleges in Delaware and Missouri have almost a complete control over the determination of the activities the districts are to undertake. The districts in these states are given only three powers which they are to exercise in independence of the state colleges: those of entering into agreements; furnishing materials, equipment, and financial aid to farmers; and accepting contributions of money, services, and materials. All other powers of the districts were implied from the grant of the general power to promote all reasonable measures for saving soil. But this power is limited by the requirement that all such measures shall be in general agreement with those currently advocated by the college of agriculture for saving the productive power of farm land. Clearly state colleges with such powers could, if they so desired, block any real national programming in district conservation administration.

Causes of Extension-SCS Friction

The indication that the Extension Services are in strategic position to block or distort national programming does not mean that the Extensions have generally acted to do so. In only a half dozen states are SCS-Extension working relationships apparently completely unsatisfactory. On the other hand, in a majority of the states Extension-SCS relations are usually rated as productively cooperative.

Extension reactions to the impact of the federal soil conservation program, in general, have followed the same attitude patterns that have developed in their relationships with other federal action programs. Basic in Extension attitudes is their state institutional fear of being squeezed out by the new federal-local axis in agriculture. The danger to the continuing power and influence of the state Extensions is seen as arising out of the fact that the federal action agencies are dealing directly with the farmers, pouring into the localities financial subsidies and free government services such as technical assistance, machinery, seeds, and so on. This encroachment by action agencies upon the Extension's traditional prerogative of dealing directly with the farmer was railed against by the former Farm Bureau president, Edward O'Neal:

> Instead of using the agencies and instrumentalities which were already functioning and in contact with the great majority of farmers, the Soil Conservation Service built up its own organization and administrative machinery to reach out into the States and counties, and deal directly with individual farmers.[27]

The fact that the county personnel of an action agency like SCS often outnumber Extension workers in a county heightens

---

[27] House Appropriation *Hearings,* 1947, *op. cit.,* p. 1633.

the threat of Extensions' losing their farmer supports. Although it is commonly observed that the attitudes of county Extension workers are generally colored by the attitudes of the state office, the frequent fear of the individual county agent that federal workers will take over his job in the county also builds into the total state Extension reaction. The outnumbering of the Extension people in the county is often pointed out by Extension personnel.

The threat to the Extension's work and influence in the state is said to be aggravated by the practical impossibility of separating the jurisdictions of education and operations. Although the Extension's jurisdiction in the field of agricultural education has been fully recognized by the Department, the boundaries between education and operations, in the functioning of an agricultural program, are confused and interpenetrating. As O. R. Zeasman, the Wisconsin Extension conservationist explained:

Washington memoranda sharply divide conservation education and farm planning. That is impossible. Planning a farm is unavoidably educational work. Educational work, if effective, must include demonstrations that include planning.

In continuing, he voiced the typical attitude of the majority of Extensions: "I am not jealous of the overlap and I don't think you [SCS personnel] are. We are both interested in securing more soil conservation on land in Wisconsin."[28]

There are, however, Extensions which see a threat in this overlap. A former Georgia Extension official summed this feeling up thus: "There are those who think that the Extension Service is again in danger. That some of the new services which closely duplicate features of the regular Extension Programs will gradually supplant it."[29] The past president of the American Farm Bureau saw in the overlapping of functions of the SCS and the Extensions an unreasonable encroachment into Extension territory:

The fact is that the services of the Soil Conservation Service consist almost entirely of pesonal services of employees who furnish technical and advisory assistance, demonstrations in conservation practices and

---

[28] O. R. Zeasman, "Soil Conservation Educational Program for Winter Months," 1945, p. 1.

[29] J. A. Evans, *Recollections of Extension History*, North Carolina State College Extension Circular, No. 224, August 1938, p. 45.

land-use planning — the things for which the agricultural extension service of the respective states were intended to provide.[30]

In line with this thinking, Extension directors sometimes make the point that conservation farming is no more than good farm management and that the farm conservation plan is, or should be if it is to be practical, a farm management plan.

In short, agricultural education may with logic be so defined that its jurisdication includes almost all of the government's agricultural activity in a county. Therefore, in honesty, Extension staffs may believe that they should be in charge of all planning for each agricultural activity which comes into the county. The Missouri Extension director put the proposition thus:

> This [farm] plan must be the farmer's own plan. It is an educational process. Unless the farmer and his family understand and agree upon each step in the plan, it will not be carried through to successful completion. A farm plan can be made more quickly by an expert, but unless the farmer himself works it through and understands each step, it is simply a paper plan to be stuck up behind the clock and worth no more than the paper on which it is written. This is one of the many reasons why we so strongly endorse the recommendations of the American Farm Bureau Federation Board of Directors, that planning work be done by the State Colleges and the Extension Services because they are logically charged with the responsibility for educational work with farm families.[31]

The possible grounds for friction between SCS and Extension personnel because of the overlapping in the jurisdictions of education and operations in conservation activity have sometimes not been lessened by the attitudes of the SCS staff. The SCS sometimes has not given its best efforts to getting along with the Extensions. In the counties, the Extensions frequently have felt that SCS personnel have ridden rough shod into the educational work in conservation. They resent claims that: "The agent is dragging his feet and the program can't wait." County agents often resent the undeniably possessive attitude of the SCS technicians toward the districts. In indicating problems in Extension-SCS relationships, Extension directors have mentioned county agents' reporting that after the agent had taken the lead in establishing a district, SCS personnel then

---

[30] House Appropriation *Hearings,* 1947, *op. cit.,* p. 1633.

[31] J. W. Burch, "Balanced Farming," address before American Farm Bureau Federation Annual Convention, December 11, 1946, San Francisco, California, mimeographed and distributed by the American Farm Bureau, p. 5.

took the district completely over, excluding the agent from its operation. One Extension director voiced this resentment:

As actually in operation in the field, under our agreement with the Soil Conservation Service, the Extension Service in the State largely becomes the free horse on which the Soil Conservation Service is riding. We do the propaganda work to set up the machinery and then it passes out of our hands. When the criticism, however, comes from the field, the Extension Service is the one that gets the blame.

Probably the most common cause of disagreement between the Extensions and SCS arises out of a three-step Extension attitude, which is healthful for the conservation program. The state colleges, with their accumulation of experience in scientific agricultural methods, realize that they are well equipped with technical knowledge in conservation. They feel that their years of working with farmers have given them insight into the best administrative procedure to use in getting farmers into a program. The opinions which they independently develop will not always agree with SCS doctrine. Therefore, they feel it proper and necessary that their opinions also carry weight in the making of conservation determinations.

Extension-SCS Cooperation

The differing of opinions between federal and state agencies is a healthy development in a federalized administration. If mechanisms can be developed through which such diverging views can be threshed out to produce a common program, these differing opinions should bring about a sounder and better proportioned approach to conservation than if the SCS or the Extension Service alone made all determinations in guiding and advising the districts.

In general, the state Extensions and the Soil Conservation Service have worked to develop cooperative arrangements and techniques for purposefully joining their efforts to aid farmers in getting conservation on their lands. The state advisory committees, which were set up to perform the over-all coordinating function within each state, have not been particularly active. As already mentioned, the inactivity of a majority of these committees does not mean that the coordinating work is not being carried on.

The joint employment by SCS and Extension of an Extension soil conservationist in 29 states has been the most fruitful mechanism for developing cooperative efforts in soil conservation education. Although administratively responsible to the director of Extension, he is in constant touch through correspondence and personal contacts with SCS thinking. He has close and continuous contacts with the county agents. The stages in the evolution of the office of Extension conservationist reveal how it has developed from a rather primitive mechanism into a somewhat sophisticated instrument of coordination.

When the job was first created, the Extension conservationist was to be a sort of propagandist to aid in bringing about district creation. His work methods were direct. He shuttled over the state, personally holding meetings, tours, and demonstrations. In the second stage of development, the Extension conservationist became a sort of trouble shooter, even lackey boy, being sent here and there into the districts to try to smooth out Service technician-county agent relations. Still his method was the direct approach.

In recent years, however, the Extension conservationist has been developing into a planner of the total educational phases of the district program. He is being discouraged from acting as the direct agent, holding demonstrations, tours, and so on. Rather, he has the responsibility of developing the over-all scheme for accomplishing the educational and servicing jobs. He is to work out objectives and procedures which are to guide the county agents and SCS technicians. He feeds them material, exhorts them to greater effort, and gives them guiding advice. As the Extension conservationists' function has now developed they are making a major contribution to developing unity of effort through:

(1) Their assistance to the State Soil Conservation Advisory Committees and other State Committees
(2) Leadership in development of a State plan for soil conservation education
(3) Assisting county agents and others working with soil conservation district governing bodies to develop plans for educational work
(4) Assisting workers within districts to develop and secure needed materials and to choose and use effectively the best suited techniques for carrying the districts' educational program into effect.[32]

[32] Statement prepared by G. E. Riddell, for use by M. L. Wilson in Agricultural Appropriation *Hearings,* 1948, March 11, 1947.

EMERGENCE OF STATE SOIL CONSERVATION COMMITTEES

The legal state soil conservation committee will play an important part in determining how the soil conservation district can be geared into the larger conservation movement. In the first place, it has definite legal authority to determine whether a district shall be organized and to appoint farmers to district boards. Although there are considerable variations among the state laws, thirty-four states provide for the appointment of one or more of the supervisors, usually by the state committee. It also has certain operational controls over the district.

The districts, as set up under the standard act, were to be after their creation almost entirely free of state committee operational control. From the enumeration of the committee's powers in the standard act, it is clear that the newly created state agency was to act as a facilitating rather than a control agency. Section 4 of the standard act provides:

In addition to the duties and powers hereinafter conferred upon the State soil conservation committee, it shall have the following duties and powers:

(1) To offer such assistance as may be appropriate to the supervisors of soil conservation districts, organized as provided hereinafter, in the carrying out of any of their powers and programs

(2) To keep the supervisors of each of the several districts organized under the provisions of this act informed of the activities and experience of all other districts organized hereunder, and to facilitate an interchange of advice and experience between such districts and cooperation between them

(3) To coordinate the programs of the several soil conservation districts organized hereunder so far as this may be done by advice and consultation

(4) To secure the cooperation and assistance of the United States and any of its agencies, and of agencies of this State, in the work of such districts

(5) To disseminate information throughout the State concerning the activities and programs of the soil conservation districts organized hereunder, and to encourage the formation of such districts in areas where their organization is desirable.

There has been some trend in state legislation, however, to give the state committees operational authorities over the district not envisioned in the standard act. Under the New Hampshire law, which declares the entire state to be a soil conservation district, all district powers are granted to the state committee. The exercise of these powers, in part, is delegated by the state committee to sub-districts. Connecticut, which does not provide for districts in its law, grants general powers to the Commissioner of Farms and Markets. As in New Hampshire, some of these powers are delegated to local work areas. Thus, the state body in these states may exercise a complete operational control over the districts, if it should so choose.

All of the major powers granted the districts in Georgia and Oregon are conditional upon the pleasure or approval of the state committee. In West Virginia, the districts can carry on research, develop district plans, and prescribe the various types of land-use regulations only with the approval of the state committee. In Wisconsin, the approval of the state committee is necessary for districts to carry out preventive and control measures, enter into agreements, furnish materials, equipment and financial aid, develop plans, accept contributions of money, services and materials, and impose conditions on the extension of benefits. Districts in New York, Illinois, and Pennsylvania may not publish district plans without the approval of the state committee.

In some states, additional operational controls by the state committees over district activities are spelled out. Michigan districts may accept contributions of money, services, and materials from state and federal agencies subject to such policies and procedures as adopted by the state committee. Missouri, as already mentioned, gives its state committee an almost complete operational control over the activities of the districts. First, the state committee may withhold state aid to districts not complying with the policies of the State soil districts commission in any matter under the provisions of the act. Secondly, district rules, regulations, forms and other documents, are subject to the commission's approval. Third, farmer-district agreements and contracts are subject to the commission's approval. Fourth, the use and expenditure of moneys and materials granted the district from the federal government must be in accordance with commission policies. Finally, contracts and legal instruments are subject to the commission's approval.

These control authorities of the state committees have the dual effect of necessitating a close administrative relationship between the districts and the committee and making the relationship between SCS and the district more indirect. The buffer role of the state committee between SCS and the district is most definite and unmistakable in Connecticut, Missouri, New Hampshire, and Pennsylvania. In these states, the basic memorandum of understanding with the Department of Agriculture is signed by the state agency rather than by each individual district, as is the practice in other states. The supplemental memorandum of understanding in these states is a tri-partite agreement among the Service, the state conservation agency, and the individual district — as contrasted with direct SCS-district agreements in other states.

This tendency for the states to increase the power of their state committees has been a trend which has only gotten into movement in recent years. The original enabling acts of Missouri, Connecticut, and New Hampshire all have been passed since 1943. Michigan and Pennsylvania, in 1945, strengthened their committees by legal amendments.

Although the Wisconsin law, in 1937, set an early precedent for the establishment of a strong state committee, it remained for Missouri some seven years later firmly to establish the state committee as a funnel for SCS-district relationships. In the fiscal 1945 Agriculture Department Appropriation Act, the following proviso was inserted in the SCS portion of the Act:

Provided further, That in the State of Missouri where the State has established a central State agency authorized to enter into agreements with the United States or any of its agencies on policies and general programs for the saving of its soil by the extension of Federal aid to any soil conservation district in such State, the agreements made by or on behalf of the United States with any such soil conservation district shall have the prior approval of such central State agency before they shall become effective as to such district.[33]

This proviso sometimes is referred to as the Cannon Amendment, and also as the Second Missouri Compromise.

In addition to the state committees' gaining legal operational controls over the districts, they also are beginning to tie the districts to them through their power over the distribution of the mounting financial aids the states are giving the districts. In some states, the state agency has almost complete discretion in determining how the state appropriation is to be allocated to the districts. For example, in Pennsylvania, funds so allocated shall be apportioned ". . .in an equitable and just manner at

---

[33] "Department of Agriculture Appropriation Act, 1945" Public Law 367, 78th Cong., Ch. 296, 2nd Sess. This proviso has been carried as a part of the standard wording in all subsequent SCS appropriations.

Fig. 20 — Barns in South Dakota with drifted sand up to 6 feet deep in places.

Fig. 21 — Emergency cover crop planting of cane and sudan grass on area shown in Fig. 20 provided effective protection against further wind blowing and paved the way for permanent stabilization and reoccupaten of the farm under preper soil and moisture-saving farming methods.

the discretion of the commissioner, and the decision of the commissioner shall be final."

In Nebraska, the state committee is to allocate funds ". . .on an acreage or other basis." In Vermont and South Carolina, such flexible standards as "fair, reasonable, in the public interest, due consideration to total acreage, relative expense of carrying on operations, unusual topography, and severity of erosion," are to be used in making allocations. On the other hand, in other states a more exact formula for distribution is set up. For example, in Maine, up to 75 per cent of total funds are to be distributed on the acreage basis in direct proportion to the total acreage of land within each district, and the remaining 25 per cent allocated at committee discretion on the basis of reasonableness and public interest.

Another new development in state committees' materially assisting districts has occurred in a few states. The state committee in Virgina is authorized to purchase, maintain, and operate necessary machinery and equipment for soil conservation operation. "The committee shall have the custody and control of the machinery and other equipment and shall provide storage for it, and shall be available to the districts upon such terms as the committee prescribes," declares the state statute. As the volume of state material assistance to districts grows, the state committee's real control over the districts will increase.

Finally, state committee influence over the districts will increase as the committees become active in facilitating district operations. Through procedural guides, newsletters and circulars, and personal contacts, the committees will build up a guiding and assisting relationship with district supervisors which will give them a real working influence over them.

The trend toward farmer supervisor membership on state committees is probably a threat to state college control of the committees. Although farmer committee members were legally provided for on several of the state committtees organized in the early years of the district program, these farmers were usually "Extension" farmers. It is significant that all state laws providing for farmer members before 1944 — that is before the influence of the supervisors' association was felt — did not specify that such farmers were to be district supervisors.[34] Four of these states

---

[34] Illinois, New Jersey, and Wisconsin provided for farmer members in 1937; Montana, Oregon, Tennessee, Texas, and Washington, in 1939; Kentucky, in 1940; Maine, in 1941; and Delaware, Missouri, and Rhode Island, in 1943. In Texas, farmer committeemen were to be elected.

provided for "farm organization" farmers being represented upon the committees. New Jersey gave ex-officio membership to the master of the state Grange and to the president of the state Farm Bureau. Montana provided that the governor was to select one member from each of the two leading farmer organization's list of candidates. Maine specified that the Farm Bureau and the Grange were each to submit a candidate. Rhode Island provided for three Farm Bureau representatives.

In contrast, after 1944, almost all state laws providing for farmer members specified that these farmers also were to be district supervisors or representatives of the supervisors' association. The California, Michigan and Vermont laws set up the specification of being a district supervisor. Georgia, in 1945, specified that the farmer members are to be members of the Board of Directors of the Georgia Association of Soil Conservation District Supervisors. North Carolina, in 1947, added to the membership of the state committee the president, first vice-president and the immediate past president of the State Association of Soil Conservation District Supervisors. By 1952, thirty-two state committees had farmer members who were not legally designated as representatives of any farm organization. Four states — Georgia, New York, Oklahoma, and Texas — have all-farmer committees. In twelve other states, farmers constitute a majority of the committee membership.

In Oklahoma and Kentucky, Extension control over the state committee has been circumvented by the establishment of another body composed of farmer supervisors which is given many of the powers ordinarily enjoyed by a state committee. In Kentucky, in 1946, a Division of Soil and Water Resources was created in the Department of Conservation. It is staffed by nine soil conservation district supervisors, appointed from a list of candidates submitted by the supervisors from each congressional district.

In Oklahoma, the state committee was abolished in 1945, and replaced by a state soil conservation board, composed of five farmers who are soil conservation district supervisors. It is probable that the infiltration of farmer supervisors upon the state committees may remove these bodies from a dominant Extension influence in states where the supervisor association is strong. It cannot be as accurately predicted, however, that such newly constituted committees will thereby come under SCS domination.

The state committee has thus far largely been regarded as a body without an organizational personality, without institutional drives and ambitions of its own — an organ, in short, designed for state college or SCS control. Yet the factors are all present for its becoming an independent institutional personality, which will accept control from no other agency. As its power in the districts grows, as it has increasing funds to dispense, as it develops its own organization and staff, as it gains its own organized popular supports, it is likely to develop its own organizational interest and views in conservation activity. The executive secretary of one state committee pointed out: "The committee is not going to be a Charlie McCarthy to anyone."

The Soil Conservation Service generally has been quite successful in using the state committees as agents for distributing information and materials to supervisors to facilitate district operations. Yet, as the state committees and their staffs work with these materials, explaining district problems to supervisors through correspondence and in person, it is natural that the committees will develop independent views on what are necessary minimum essentials in a district conservation program, how the program can best be effected, and so on.

The changing character of the personnel of the state committees is the strongest portent of the committees' becoming strong and independent institutions in their own right. The SCS probably has seen the presence of farmer supervisors on the state committees as a means of getting friendly reception of its ideas by that body. However, the development of close committee-supervisor association relationships may not only increase the committee's strength as a state body outside of other agency control, it may also put the committee under the hand of the supervisors' association.

RISE OF DISTRICT SUPERVISORS' ASSOCIATIONS

The rising influence of the supervisors' associations in conservation politics has been favorably regarded by the SCS. Just as the Extensions have had the Farm Bureau to give them organized group support in this era of pressure politics, the SCS sees in the supervisors' associations the same type of organized nationwide popular support in the national and state legislatures.

Thus far the supervisors' associations have served the Service well. They have acted as pressure organizations in national and state legislatures to get public funds for conservation activity and to maintain SCS administrative control over the national end of the district soil conservation program. Each state association has a standing legislative committee which considers conservation measures that should be brought before its state legislature. The national association watches Congress. The late president of the national association put an open face on this activity of the association:

> It amuses me to see the "soft pedal" put on when mention is made of "politics" or "politicians" as an instrument of assistance. Let us face the fact squarely that one does not obtain government assistance of any nature by going around a representative, for that assistance comes through him and his efforts. Our representatives in the State and National Congress are there to serve us. And, how can they render the best service unless they know the problem confronting the people and what is being done to solve it? Therefore, I have made an earnest endeavor to acquaint our representatives with the true agricultural condition in the South and with problems, as well as with the instruments, soil conservation districts, with which to combat them. . . . Each of our national representatives has been contacted several times and an attempt made to give them full information as to our purpose, objectives and activities.[35]

The president of the national association speaks for supervisors and their districts in Congressional agricultural hearings. He usually brings representatives of the state associations to speak with him. The state associations send resolutions to Congress.

Supervisors' associations have been instrumental in saving SCS from serious appropriation cuts. Within each state the state associations probably are responsible for the steadily mounting state appropriations to districts. The supervisors' associations have been powerful in the effort to block the Farm Bureau's drive to place the administration of the national conservation program in the hands of the state Extensions. When the Hill-Cooley Bill for giving the conservation program over to the Extensions was threatening in Congress, practically all of the state supervisors' associations, at the instigation of their national

[35] E. C. McArthur, then president of the South Carolina Association of Soil Conservation District Supervisors, Annual Report, January 18, 1945, p. 3.

office, adopted resolutions supporting the SCS as the appropriate agency for administering conservation. To quote only one:

Oklahoma: Be it further resolved: that soil conservation districts must be kept free and independent; that the bureau of the Soil Conservation Service is a proper and necessary corollary to the efficient functioning of such districts and that the envy excited in other quarters is ample proof of the success attained by the district movement.

Be it further resolved: that we view with suspicion and alarm the reach of the greedy hands of the American Farm Bureau Federation in collaboration with Extension Service, or vice-versa, for power and direction over the destiny of the whole conservation field; that this wolf in sheep's clothing attack is made under the pretext of economy and efficiency, to hide the real purpose and design to fashion a strangle hold on the farms and farmers of this State and Nation.

We therefore recommend that the present soil conservation district program and present Soil Conservation Service be continued without change.

E. C. McArthur testified thus at the Senate agricultural appropriation hearings for fiscal 1948:

But the districts and their National Association of Soil Conservation Districts recognize the necessity of a national agency working on soil conservation and rendering the kind of assistance to districts throughout the country that the Soil Conservation Service is now making available.

We are, therefore, strongly opposed to any combining or consolidation of the Soil Conservation Service with the Extension Service, or with any other agency.

There is more than enough for both services to do, each in its respective field.[36]

When, in 1951, Senator Aiken brought before Congress the proposals of the Citizens Committee for the Hoover Report for reorganization of the Department of Agriculture, the supervisors' association was once again on hand to protect the position of the Soil Conservation Service.[37]

In the course of their promoting the cause of soil conservation and protecting the jurisdiction of the Soil Conservation Service, the supervisors' associations themselves have been building up as powers in state conservation administration. The associations, through their representatives on state soil conservation committees, are gaining a strategic position in the legal administra-

[36] Senate Appropriation *Hearings,* 1948, *op. cit.,* p. 1114.

[37] U. S. Congress. Senate Committee on Expenditures in the Executive Departments. *Hearings* on S. 1149, 82nd Cong., 1st Sess., pp. 269–281, 476, 477.

tion of the program. Their influence with the national and state legislatures gives them weight in their dealings with the conservation agencies. Finally, the associations' influence and power with the supervisors in their individual districts is their greatest control over district administration.

Perhaps this growing power of the national and state associations is potentially the strongest block to national programming. Although thus far the associations have been amenable to SCS guidance and suggestions, as their power grows the associations may not remain so tractable. There are at least two potential obstacles to a national conservation program inherent in the supervisors' associations. The first is that, like other organizing of farmers locally around an agency program, the vested interests of the supervisors, more powerful through their association, will prevent necessary functional coordination of agency activities at the national level. Thus, the district, designed as a device for coordination, might in the end act as a block to coordination.

Only the threat of a Congressional reorganization which would more seriously jeopardize the district's position in the federal conservation program has made the supervisors' association agreeable to the Secretary's program for coordinating the activities of SCS and the ACP branch of PMA.[38] Nor have the supervisors been hesitant in keeping their dissatisfaction before the Secretary. Secretary Brannan's April, 1952 memorandum, declaring that it is in the national interest for every farm and every acre of farm land to be in soil conservation districts and that it is the Department's ultimate objective to assist every farmer to put a complete farm plan into effect, was in part, at least, in direct response to the pressure of the supervisors' organization. The memorandum closes with the sentence: "I shall furnish a copy to the President of the National Association of Soil Conservation Districts."

The developing power of the supervisors in the state conservation committees and in state legislatures may wrest the conservation program out of the hands of all regularly constituted government agencies, with their well-established responsibilities to an executive and to the legislature, and give it to the bureaucracy of a group organization with responsibilities only to its special membership. The fact that the local district

---

[38] *Ibid.*, p. 273.

governing bodies do not always have their roots in a truly democratic process for their selection and control, makes this danger even more real.

The fashioners of the district device intended that the district should be democratic in its operation. All states, except Alabama, New York, and Pennsylvania, provide for the election of one or more of their district supervisors. Another characteristic of local democracy also is generally observed. District supervisors are made legally responsible to the local electorate.

Although the basic desire to make the district democratic is clear, the district faces several obstacles in achieving this objective. In the first place, participation in district elections, except in the rarest and most unusual circumstances, has been very light. This, however, is not a problem peculiar to the district. Voter non-participation is a crucial problem for all political units in the United States.

The problem of devising thoroughly democratic nomination procedures has yet to be solved in most districts. Too often the nominees for the position of district supervisor are handpicked by local professional workers. The merits of a democratic election are seriously limited when the voters are given no real choice among candidates. Again, the problem of developing thoroughly democratic nomination procedures is not peculiar to the district. It is a first problem in political democracy generally, and has not been solved in the electing of a president for the United States. It is a particularly difficult problem, however, when the office involved is not highly coveted or contested.

Finally, the most serious limitation on the district's democratic nature is the sharp legal restrictions the states have placed upon the voting privilege. Although the standard act suggested to the states by the federal government would have given the vote in district matters to non-owner operators as well as to landowners. the state laws have altered this provision. In 29 states only landowners are allowed to vote on the question of establishing a district. In 19 states only landowners can vote in elections to choose district governing officials. Of the 32 states which authorize districts to enact land-use regulations, 22 permit only landowners to vote on the question of their adoption.

Those states which have restricted district voting privileges to the landowning group obviously felt that owners alone should have control of matters which so directly affect the use of their land. This is a decision which only the state legislatures are legally competent to make. However, any such restriction is out of keeping with the principles of American democracy, which long since advanced beyond the stage of requiring property ownership as a basis for voting.

Districts' Continuing Capacity to Assist Farmers

Another important determinant of the district's role in the future conservation movement is the services and resources the district will have to offer farmers. When the district first came into conservation it offered labor, equipment on an easy rental basis, planting stock, and technical services to cooperating farmers. During the depression some of the labor of the Civilian Conservation Corps was made available to cooperating farmers through the district. The CCC provided men and machinery in the damming of gullies, building of terraces, and so on. After the disbanding of the camps, their machinery was parcelled out by SCS among the districts on a loan basis for use by district farmers. In the early days of the district, considerable machinery was made available to the district through Congressional appropriation.

Today, however, the federal furnishing of machinery has dwindled to a minimum. As already pointed out, no Congressional appropriation for machinery has been made since 1947. Increasingly the districts have been relying on contract equipment in district conservation work. The district does not furnish the farmer with the equipment. Rather, it acts as an agent in bringing the contractor and the farmer together. Whereas the rates for the use of district-operated equipment are kept at a minimum, the rate a farmer working through the district must pay a contractor is not significantly lower than if he engaged the contractor independently of the district. The SCS has been reducing to a minimum its distribution of planting stock.

In short, technical assistance in planning and applying conservation practices is now the only important federally contributed resource which the districts have to offer farmers. The Secretary's 1951 memorandum directing SCS to provide technical assistance to ACP farmers, regardless of whether they are district cooperators, constitutes a threat to the district's continuing as an important part of the federal conservation program. If a farmer can receive the assistance of SCS field technicians for the one practice in which he is interested without becoming a district cooperator, it might be more difficult to persuade him to commit himself to completing a long series of practices. The Soil Conservation Service, however, is determined that its new technical responsibilities in the ACP program shall not weaken the district movement.

Its first effort has been to obtain a staff of professional and semi-professional personnel adequate to meet the requests of both ACP clients and district cooperators. During the first few months after SCS was given the task of providing ACP farmers with technical assistance, district supervisors felt that their program of technical assistance to district cooperators was impaired. The ACP funds and PMA semi-professional employees transferred to SCS to use in carrying its technical responsibilities in the ACP program did not provide enough additional staff to carry the extra load. It has been estimated that it cost SCS between $2,500,000 and five million dollars in technical time to provide ACP farmers with assistance during the fiscal year of 1952. This cost, district supervisors and their associations felt, was at the expense of the district program. Secretary Brannan's April, 1952 memorandum was in part a direct response to this supervisor dissatisfaction. He specified that:

Arrangements should be worked out as rapidly as possible, making use of existing provisions of law and such other arrangements as may be developed, whereby the SCS can handle this added responsibility without impairing the technical assistance that SCS is furnishing to soil conservation districts.

Although the Secretary's directives do not insist that farmers receive their technical assistance through the district, SCS is attempting to devise arrangements whereby almost all of its technical time can be channeled through the districts. SCS in its 1953 budget request asks for an additional $3,500,000 to provide technical assistance to new districts and to give additional assistance to old districts where technical assistance has been inadequate.

It is not probable, however, as some SCS officials had hoped, that SCS can continue to assign all of the time of its field technicians completely to the districts, which, in turn, would allocate it among district cooperators and ACP farmers. Under such an arrangement, the ACP farmer or the PMA committee would have to come to the district to ask for assistance.

The Service hopes to solve the problem of priority between ACP clients and district cooperators by eventually bringing almost all ACP farmers into the district fold. It views the reorganization as an opportunity for expanding district activity, for bringing five million additional farm operators into the district program. With such an inclusive membership, the question of priorities as between district cooperators and non-cooperators would no longer exist.

SCS is using two approaches in its effort to bring ACP farmers into the district program. The first is to place the total federal conservation program on a high level of technical standards. The objective of SCS is to obtain the development of such technically adequate county agricultural resources conservation programs that farmers can be easily persuaded to come into the district. The task is to convince the joint conservation policy making groups at the national, state, and county levels that technical assistance and payments for the permanent type conservation treatments should be given only when the proposed work is technically sound. This would often entail the carrying out of a combination of conservation treatments.

The Service and the district have two opportunities for facilitating the development of such joint programs. In the first place, they are to be members of the joint groups preparing the programs. Secondly, SCS field technicians, after on-site inspection, have the authority to approve or disapprove a proposed treatment for technical assistance and conservation payments. The technician's decision is to be made not only on the grounds that the proposed work can be properly designed, safely and economically established, but that, in his judgment, it will ". . . fit into a conservation plan for the entire farm or ranch when such is developed. He should determine also that the practice is not dependent for permanency on the prior establishment of other needed conservation practices and measures."[39] Moreover, SCS is to give technical guidance and supervision to an ACP client only when the entire practice is going to be completed by the farmer:

When PMA assigns employees or transfers funds to help SCS in

---

[39] Memorandum from H. H. Bennett, April 9, 1951, *op. cit.*

respect to any of these four categories of technical guidance and supervision [planning, layout, installing conservation structures, and applying conservation practices] it should be understood that this assistance applies to whole practices and not to any given portion of a practice, even though the ACP assistance approved for the farm is sufficient to pay only a portion of the cost of the practice. For example, if a farmer is putting in a drainage ditch that will cost $500 and ACP has approved payment of $150 on the practice, it is intended to reimburse the farmer for a part of the cost of the whole ditch. The personnel or funds made available to SCS by PMA could be used to perform the necessary technical functions on the entire ditch.[40]

The first step the Service has taken in its program to get joint acceptance of high conservation standards has been to develop national, regional, state and county technical guide material. Such material includes information about major problem areas, land-use capability classes and units, and minimum recommendations for use and specifications for treatment of each class and unit. These technical guides, SCS hopes, will be utilized fully in developing state and county programs.[41]

Officials of SCS also suggest that since most agencies actually participated in the development of existing district programs and work plans they might well be the basis of the total county program. In some cases, it is suggested, they might actually serve as the county program. They also believe that county plans might well set the objective of a farm plan on every farm and list specific steps which would lead to a farm plan. "To insure the acceptance and use of high technical standards and to aid SCS in carrying out its responsibility for furnishing technical assistance," State and county ACP handbooks are to include specifications for those practices for which SCS has the technical responsibility. These specifications become a legal requirement for the practices and govern the checking of performance. Specifications before they are included in the ACP handbooks must be cleared by the appropriate regional SCS office.[42]

For their part, the districts are to bend their efforts toward bringing every ACP farmer into the district program with commitments to complete the combined conservation treatment for his farm. As already indicated, the districts, at SCS suggestion,

---

[40] SCS Field Memorandum 1144, "General Operating Procedures for Use by SCS in Carrying Out Its Responsibility in the Agricultural Conservation Program," from Robert M. Salter, February 20, 1952.

[41] Memorandum from R. H. Musser, SCS Region III, to All Ranking Field Officers, April 9, 1951.

[42] Memorandum from R. M. Salter, February 20, 1952, *op. cit.*

have eased their requirement of the complete farm plan in order to permit a maximum number of farmers to begin cooperating with the districts at once. SCS technicians and district supervisors are actively encouraging ACP participants to become district cooperators. The range of SCS assistance which will be available to a farmer after he has signed up is being spelled out. As the former chief of the Service put it, the technician ". . . should explain to each ACP participant the advantages of becoming a district cooperator."[43]

During the latter half of 1951, farmers were coming into the district program at the rate of about 10,000 a month. Some 68,000 new cooperators, operating 25,000,000 acres, were in the initial or advanced stages of planning in January, 1952. Regional officials have recently indicated that the great majority of ACP clients seeking SCS technical assistance for the 1952 program year are becoming district cooperators. Thus the clienteles of the ACP program and of the districts may soon become virtually identical.

With such an inclusive district membership, the problem of priorities as between district cooperators and ACP farmers would become unimportant. However, the question of priorities for assistance to farmers in the initial, advanced, or final stages of conservation planning would still remain. As district cooperators, farmers wanting only one practice would be subject to schedules of assistance set up by district boards. If a district board had determined to concentrate the SCS technical assistance made available to it upon individuals developing basic plans for their farms, could a district cooperator, wanting only a single practice, go outside the district and seek immediate assistance as an ACP client? Even this type of priority problem, however, will become unimportant if sufficient technical assistance becomes available for servicing all requests for technically suitable practices.

Whatever the priorities which are finally worked out may be, the element of obligation and coercion in SCS-district and district-farmer relationships is fast disappearing. The district's success in getting the county agricultural resources conservation committee to accept a conservation program of high technical adequacy depends upon its ability to sell rather than to coerce. Nor can the district continue to demand that a farmer accept a long series of obligations as the price for becoming a district cooperator. For, if SCS assistance is to be available to ACP partici-

---

[43] Memorandum from H. H. Bennett, April 9, 1951, *op. cit.*

pants not under agreement with the district, the district no longer holds a monopoly on technical assistance, which could be held out as a reward for accepting a complete farm plan. Thus, the large question still remains: How will farmers be led to carry out complete and adequate conservation programs on their lands? It may be that under the new arrangements for extending federal technical assistance to farmers, the Secretary or even Congress itself will have to establish a policy for giving assistance only to those farmers who are making progress in the development of complete conservation programs on their farms.

An analysis of the district's capacity to provide farmers with services in conservation which they need and want cannot rest with the appraisal of the possibilities of continuing federal resources being put into their programs. For the districts no longer depend entirely upon the extension of federal assistance. The district was developed as a mechanism which could obtain material assistance from a variety of public agencies, private groups and individuals. Although only the districts of two states have the taxing power, and districts generally are prohibited from borrowing money, they have through a variety of local means built up their resources in equipment, planting stock, administrative personnel, and sub-professional technical assistance in applying conservation practices.

The most significant development which may aid the districts to grow in number and strength is the increase of state assistance to the districts. Although state appropriations do not begin to meet the federal cost of furnishing the districts technical assistance, they may, as they increase, enable the district to furnish those extra services which will convince farmers that they should come into the district program.

The local soil conservation district, in the time measurements of public governing arrangements, is still a young institution. But even in its immaturity it has been making systematic progress in working out one of the critical dilemmas in organizing modern democratic government: the need for the central programming of a governmental activity, which is national in its nature and scope, versus the need for bringing into such public action that local government which is probably basic in keeping democratic governing vigorous and in tapping the energies and resources of citizens as individuals.

The district device is propositioned upon the belief that

neither centralized national programming nor local determination is alone the most effective method of administering a national public activity. Rather it is based upon the belief that the functionings of national and local government must be so integrated as to permit the blending and utilization of the peculiar attributes, competencies, and resources of each level of government. The working process which the district device is now evolving is one of the forward steps being taken in developing arrangements and procedures for accomplishing such a constructive integration.

The soil conservation district has not yet been sufficiently weathered by time for its value in future agricultural administration to be projected. Thus far, however, the district has demonstrated promising potentialities in developing a new working integration between national and local government, as well as between the lay citizen and his government. Already the cross-fertilization of national and local experiences, which is taking place through the district mechanism, is resulting in a sounder and better proportioned approach to conservation activity than if either level of government were attempting to go it alone.

Appendix

Citations of State Soil Conservation Districts' Laws

State	Approved or Filed	Session Laws Citation	Code Citation
1. Alabama	March 18, 1939	General Acts Ala. 1939, Act 147, p. 202	Code of Ala. 1940, Tit. 2, Sec.
	August 16, 1949	Acts of Ala. 1949, Act 382, p. 558	658—670
2. Arizona	March 17, 1941	Ariz. Laws of 1941, c. 43, p. 79	Ariz. Code Ann. 1939, (1949 Cum.
	March 5, 1945	Sess. Laws Ariz. 1945, c. 31, p. 45	Supp.) Sec. 75–1701—75–714
3. Arkansas	March 3, 1937	Acts of Ark. 1937, Act 197, p. 695	Ark. Stats. 1947 Ann. Sec. 9–901—
	March 24, 1943	Acts of Ark. 1943, Act 354, p. 786	9–913
	March 20, 1945	Acts of Ark. 1945, Act 225, p. 518	
	March 28, 1947	Acts of Ark. 1947, Act 338, p. 765	
4. California	March 29, 1938	Stat. of Calif. 1938, c. 7, p. 48	Deering's Calif. Codes—Public
	May 29, 1939	Stat. of Calif. 1939, c. 312, p. 1584	Resources, Div. 9, Sec. 9000—9606
	Feb. 28, 1940	Stat. of Calif. 1941, First Extra Session of 1940, c. 21, p. 45	
	April 6, 1943	Stat. of Calif. 1943, c. 66, p. 305	
	May 31, 1943	c. 900, p. 2747	
	May 31, 1943	c. 929, p. 2801	
	May 23, 1945	Stat. of Calif. 1945, c. 423, p. 909	
	June 25, 1945	c. 1031, p. 1993	
	July 9, 1945	c. 1187, p. 2239	
	May 31, 1947	Stat. of Calif. 1947, c. 472, p. 1370	
	June 3, 1947	c. 517, p. 1513	
	June 17, 1947	c. 802, p. 1891	
	July 7, 1947	c. 1118, p. 2558	
	July 11, 1947	c. 1362, p. 2913	
	July 18, 1947	c. 1555, p. 3196	
	July 18, 1947	c. 1558, p. 3198	
	July 20, 1949	Stat. of Calif. 1949, ch. 1031, p. 1892	
	July 20, 1949	ch. 1032, p. 1914	

5. Colorado	May 6, 1937	Session Laws of Colo. 1937, c. 241, p. 1169	Colo. Stat. Ann. 1935,—1949 Re-
	May 2, 1939	Session Laws of Colo. 1939, c. 160, p. 549	placement Vol. 4B, c. 149B
	April 3, 1941	Session Laws of Colo. 1941, c. 203, p. 688	
	May 3, 1945	Session Laws of Colo. 1945, c. 229, p. 624	
	May 18, 1949	Session Laws of Colo. 1949, c. 231, p. 663	
6. Connecticut	July 18, 1945	1945 Supp. to Conn. Gen. Stat., c. 106, Sec. 478h–480h, p. 202	Gen. Stats. of Conn. Rev. of 1949, Vol. II, Sec.
	June 11, 1947	1947 Supp. to Conn. Gen. Stat., c. 106, Sec. 536i, p. 229	3061—3064
7. Delaware	April 2, 1943	Laws of Del. 1943, c. 212, p. 605	Not codified
	March 25, 1947	Laws of Del. 1947, c. 87, p. 294	
8. Florida	June 10, 1937	Laws of Fla. 1937, c. 18144—(No. 438), p. 913	Fla. Stat. Ann. Sec. 582.01— 582.33
	June 12, 1939	Laws of Fla. 1939, c. 19473—(No. 478), p. 1143	
	June 6, 1947	Laws of Fla. 1947, c. 23941 (No. 327), p. 670	
	June 13, 1949	Laws of Fla. 1949, c. 25407 (No. 411), p. 995	
9. Georgia	March 26, 1937	Ga. Laws 1937, No. 339, p. 377	Code of Ga. Ann. Tit. 5, Sec.
	March 6, 1945	Ga. Laws, 1945, No. 222, p. 190	5–1801—5–2216
	Feb. 15, 1949	Ga. Laws 1949, No. 148, p. 584	
10. Idaho	March 9, 1939	Session Laws Idaho 1939, c. 200, p. 380	Idaho Code Ann. (1940 Supp.) Sec.
	March 2, 1945	Session Laws Idaho 1945, c. 94, p. 143	22–2501—22–2514
	March 1, 1949	Session Laws Idaho 1949, c. 112, p. 203	
11. Illinois	July 9, 1937	Laws of Ill. 1937, p. 10	Jones Ill. Stat.
	July 25, 1939	Laws of Ill. 1939, p. 83	Ann. Vol. 2,
	July 15, 1941	Laws of Ill. 1941, p. 12	Sec. 2.138—2.171
	July 24, 1943	Laws of Ill. 1943, Vol.1,p.14	
	July 8, 1947	Laws of Ill. 1947, p. 5	
12. Indiana	March 11, 1937	Acts of Ind. 1937, c. 232, p. 1120	Burns Ind. Stat. Ann. Sec.
	March 10, 1941	Acts of Ind. 1941, c. 164, p. 500	15–1801—15–1818
	March 9, 1945	Acts of Ind. 1945, c. 331, p. 1533	

13. Iowa	May 25, 1939	Acts Reg. Session 48 G. A. Iowa, c. 92, p. 155	Iowa Code Ann. Sec. 160.1–160.12
	April 16, 1941	Acts Reg. Session 49 G. A. Iowa, c. 119, p. 132	Renumbered by Code Editor in 1951 Pocket Part
	April 10, 1941 March 17, 1949	c. 120, p. 138 Acts Reg. Session 53 G. A. Iowa, c. 207, p. 288	467 A.1–467 A.12
	Apirl 28, 1949	Acts Reg. Session 53 G. A. Iowa, c. 208, p. 289	
14. Kansas	April 2, 1937	Laws of Kan. 1937, c. 5, p. 11	Gen. Stat. of Kan. 1935 (1947
	March 30, 1945	Laws of Kan. 1945, c. 4, p. 9	Supp.), Sec. 2–1901—2–1918
15. Kentucky	March 11, 1940 March 14, 1946	Ky. Acts 1940, c. 8, p. 37 Ky. Acts 1946, c. 27, Sec. 37, p. 49	Ky. Rev. Stat. 1946, Sec. 262.010 —262.600
	March 23, 1946 March 25, 1950	c. 83, p. 186 Ky. Acts 1950, c. 106, p. 471	
16. Louisiana	July 6, 1938	Acts State of La. 1938, Act No. 370, p. 918	Dart's La. Gen. Stat. Sec. 57.7—
	July 15, 1946	Acts State of La. 1946, Act No. 137, p. 402	57.25
17. Maine	March 25, 1941	Laws of Maine 1941, c. 105, p. 141	Revised Stat. of Maine 1944, Vol.
	July 21, 1945	Laws of Maine 1945, c. 109, p. 150	1, c. 29, p. 678
	August 13, 1947	Laws of Maine 1947, c. 74, p. 152	
18. Maryland	May 28, 1937	Laws of Md. 1937, c. 437, p. 854	Ann. Code of Md. 1939 and 1947
	May 2, 1941	Laws of Md. 1941, c. 804, p. 1415	Cum. Supp. Art. 2A, Sec. 45—59
	May 4, 1943	Laws of Md. 1943, c. 444, p. 510	
19. Massachusetts	June 28, 1945	Acts and Resolves Mass. 1945, c. 531, p. 521	Ann. Laws of Mass. Vol. 4,
	Feb. 21, 1947	Acts and Resolves Mass. 1947, c. 73, p. 54	Part I, c. 128B
	July 8, 1949	Acts and Resolves Mass. 1949, c. 517, p. 439	
20. Michigan	July 23, 1937	Pub. Acts Mich. 1937, No. 297, p. 552	Mich. Stat. Ann. Vol. 9, c. 110a,
	May 25, 1945	Pub. Acts Mich. 1945, No. 280, p. 456	Sec. 13.1781— 13.1798
21. Minnesota	April 26, 1937	Laws of Minn. 1937, c. 441, p. 660	Minn. Stats. Ann. and 1950 Cum.
	April 2, 1943	Laws of Minn. 1943, c. 274, p. 374	Pocket Part Sec. 40.01—40.15
	March 12, 1945	Laws of Minn. 1945, c. 95, p. 137	
	April 2, 1947	Laws of Minn. 1947, c. 194, p. 349	
	April 9, 1949	Laws of Minn. 1949, c. 347, p. 578	

22. Mississippi	April 4, 1938	Gen. Laws of Miss. 1938, c. 253, p. 567	Miss. Code 1942 Ann. Sec. 4940—4958
23. Missouri	July 23, 1943	Laws of Mo. 1943, p. 839	Mo. Rev. Stat. Ann., 1950 Cum. Pocket Part, Sec. 14431.1—14431.10
24. Montana	Feb. 28, 1939	Laws of Mont. 1939, c. 72, p. 124	Rev. Codes of Mont. 1947 Ann. Sec. 77.101—77.116
25. Nebraska	May 18, 1937	Laws of Neb. 1937, c. 8, p. 91	Rev. Stat. of Nebraska 1943, Sec. 2-1501 —2-1547
26. Nevada	March 30, 1937	Stat. of Nev. 1937, c. 212, p. 497	Nev. Comp. Laws (Supp. 1931–1941 and Supp. 1943–49) Sec. 6870.01 —6870.18
	Feb. 28, 1945	Stat. of Nev. 1945, c. 20, p. 28	
	March 27, 1947	Stat. of Nev. 1947, c. 119, p. 431	
27. New Hampshire	May 10, 1945	N. H. Laws, 1945, c. 151, p. 197	Not codified
	March 12, 1949	N. H. Laws, 1949, c. 62, p. 56	
28. New Jersey	June 2, 1937	Laws of N. J. 1937, c. 139, p. 319	N. J. Stats. Ann. 4:24-1—4:24-38
29. New Mexico	March 17, 1937	Laws of N. M. 1937, c. 219, p. 551	N. M. Stat. 1941 Ann. Sec. 48–501—48–517
	March 16, 1939	Laws of N M. 1939, c. 163, p. 353	
	April 17, 1943	Laws of N. M. 1943, c. 130, p. 310	
	March 15, 1949	Laws of N. M. 1949, c. 109, p. 255	
30. New York	April 23, 1940	Laws of N. Y. 1940, c. 727, p. 1942	McKinney's Consol. Laws of N. Y. Ann., Vol. 52B
	April 17, 1941	Laws of N. Y. 1941, c. 515, p. 1254	
	April 19, 1945	Laws of N. Y. 1945, c. 883, p. 2010	
	April 18, 1946	Laws of N. Y. 1946, c. 896, p. 704	
	March 18, 1949	Laws of N. Y. 1949, c. 201, p. 386	
	April 5, 1950	Laws of N. Y. 1950, c. 452	
31. North Carolina	March 22, 1937	Pub. Laws of N. C., Reg. Session 1937, c. 393, p. 721	Gen. Stat. of N. C. 1943 and 1949 Cum. Supp. Sec. 139–1—139–15
	April 3, 1939	Pub. Laws of N. C. Reg. Session 1939, c. 341, p. 750	
	March 5, 1943	Session Laws of N. C. 1943, c. 481, p. 538	
	Feb. 21, 1947	Session Laws of N. C. 1947, c. 131, p. 138	
	March 10, 1949	Session Laws of N. C. 1949. c. 268, p. 283	

32. North Dakota	March 16, 1937	Laws of N. D. 1937, c. 9, p. 29	N. D. Rev. Code of 1943, Vol. 1, Sec. 4–2201—4–2246
	March 16, 1939	Laws of N. D. 1939, c. 6, p. 8	
	Feb. 13, 1945	Laws of N. D. 1945, c. 42, p. 92	
	Feb. 13, 1945	c. 45, p. 94	
33. Ohio	June 5, 1941	Laws of Ohio 1941, p. 812	Page's Ohio Gen. Code Ann. Sec. 375–13—375–21
	April 26, 1945	Laws of Ohio 1945–1946, p. 89	
34. Oklahoma	April 15, 1937	Session Laws of Okla. 1936–37, c. 38, Art. 4, p. 235	Okla. Stat. Ann., Cum. Ann. Pocket Part, Tit. 2, Sec. 801—817
	April 28, 1945	Session Laws of Okla. 1945, c. 20, p. 4	
	May 17, 1947	Session Laws of Okla. 1947, c. 20, p. 11	
35. Oregon	April 6, 1939	Ore. Laws 1939, c. 555, p. 1229	Ore. Comp. Laws Ann. and Annual Pocket Parts 1943, 1944– 45, Vol. 7, Sec. 109–301—109–315
	March 4, 1941	Ore. Laws 1941, c. 185, p. 281	
	March 23, 1945	Ore. Laws 1945, c. 348, p. 559	
	May 5, 1949	Ore. Laws 1949, c. 568, p. 918	
36. Pennsylvania	July 2, 1937	Laws of Pa. 1937, No. 557, p. 2724	Purdon's Pa. Stat. Ann., 1949 Ann. Pocket Part Tit. 3, Sec. 849—864
	June 24, 1939	Laws of Pa. 1939, No. 366, p. 848	
	May 15, 1945	Laws of Pa. 1945, No. 217, p. 547	
37. Rhode Island	April 26, 1943	R. I. Acts and Resolves 1943, c. 1338, p. 167	Not codified
38. South Carolina	April 17, 1937	Acts of S. C. 1937, No. 182, p. 242	Code of Laws of S. C. Sec. 5806–101— 5806–116
	April 16, 1943	Acts of S. C. 1943, No. 211, p. 407	
	March 28, 1946	Acts of S. C. 1946, No. 575, p. 1537	
39. South Dakota	March 5, 1937	Laws of S. D. 1937, c. 19, p. 20	S. D. Code of 1939, Sec. 4.1501—4.1516
	Feb. 28, 1945	Sess. Laws of S. D. 1945, c. 13, p. 25	
	Feb. 26, 1947	Sess. Laws S. D. 1947, c. 11–14, p. 14	Adds Code Sec. 4.1517 and 4.1518
	Feb. 23, 1949	Sess. Laws of S. D., c. 10, p. 31	
	Feb. 23, 1949	Sess. Laws of S. D., c. 11, p. 31	
40. Tennessee	March 10, 1939	Pub. Acts of Tenn. 1939, c. 197, p. 754	Williams Tenn. Code Ann. Sec. 552.31—552.44
	Feb. 15, 1941	Pub. Acts of Tenn. 1941, c. 83, p. 250	
41. Texas	April 20, 1939	Tex. Gen. Laws 1939, c. 3, p. 7	Vernon's Tex. Civil Stat., Tit. 4, Art. 165a–4
	May 20, 1941	Tex. Gen. Laws 1941, c. 308, p. 491	

42. Utah	March 23, 1937	Laws of Utah 1937, c. 116, p. 213	Utah Code Ann. 1943, Sec.
	April 3, 1941	Laws of Utah, First Special Session 1941, c. 30, p. 71	82A–0–1— 82A–0–19
	March 22, 1941	Laws of Utah 1941, c. 88, p. 189	
43. Vermont	April 11, 1939	Laws of Vt. 1939, No. 246, p. 288	Vt. Stats. 1947, Tit. 29, c. 275,
	April 10, 1941	Laws of Vt. 1941, No. 202, p. 264	Sec. 6559—6298
	March 27, 1945	Laws of Vt. 1945, No. 201, p. 264	
	April 10, 1947	Laws of Vt. 1947, No. 131, p. 189	
	April 25, 1947	No. 132, p. 190	
44. Virginia	April 1, 1938	Acts of Va. 1938, c. 394, p. 724	Code of Va. 1950 and Cum. Supp.
	March 16, 1944	Acts of Va. 1944, c. 244, p. 347	Sec. 21–1—21–112
	Feb. 27, 1950	Acts of Va. 1950, c. 65, p. 76	
45. Washington	March 17, 1939	Laws of Wash. 1939, c. 187, p. 599	Rem. Rev. Stat. of Wash. Ann.,
	March 16, 1949	Laws of Wash. 1949, c. 106, p. 236	1940 Pocket Part and 1949 Supp., Sec. 10726–1— 10726–17
46. West Virginia	March 10, 1939	Acts of W. Va. Legislature 1939, c. 5, p. 19	W. Va. Code of 1943 and 1947 Supp. Sec.
	Feb. 20, 1947	Acts of W. Va. Legislature 1947, c. 9, p. 33	2193(1)— 2193(14)
47. Wisconsin	July 1, 1937	Laws of Wisc. 1937, c. 341, p. 515	Wisc. Stat. 1949, c. 92, Sec.
	August 9, 1939	Laws of Wisc. 1939, c. 323, p. 508	92.01—92.17
	Oct. 20, 1939	Laws of Wisc. 1939, c. 532, p. 925	
	June 15, 1943	Laws of Wisc. 1943, c. 303, p. 481	
	Aug. 17, 1945	Laws of Wisc. 1945, c. 559, Sec. 9, p. 999	
	Aug. 3, 1949	Laws of Wisc. 1949, c. 619, p. 555	
48. Wyoming	March 5, 1941	Sess. Laws of Wyo. 1941, c. 134, p. 191	Wyoming Comp. Stats. 1945 and
	Jan. 27, 1945	Sess. Laws of Wyo. 1945, c. 6, p. 5	1949 Cum. Supp. Sec. 34–1401—
	Feb. 24, 1947	Sess. Laws of Wyo. 1947, c. 140, p. 168	34–1417

TABLE 1
SERVICES PROVIDED DISTRICTS BY STATE SOIL CONSERVATION COMMITTEES, 1951 [1]

State	Literature To Explain SCD Law, To Guide Farmers in Setting Up District	"Handbook" To Guide Public Employees in Setting Up District	"Handbook" on District Administration for Supervisors	System for District Handling of Finances	Assistance in Setting Up Financial System, Bond-officers, Auditing Accounts, etc.
Ala.	Yes	Yes	Yes	Yes	Yes
Ariz.	Yes	No[3]	Yes	No	No
Ark.[2]	....	....	....	....	....
Calif.[6]	Yes	Yes	Yes	No	Yes
Colo.	Yes	Yes	Yes	Yes	Yes
Conn.	No	No	No	No	No[3]
Del.	No	No	No[3]	No	No
Fla.	Yes	Yes	Yes	Yes	No[3]
Ga.	Yes	Yes	No	No	No
Idaho	Yes	Yes	Yes	No	No
Ill.	Yes	Yes	Yes	No	No
Ind.	Yes	Yes	No	Yes	Yes
Iowa	Yes	No[3]	Yes	Yes	Yes
Kan.	Yes	No	Yes	Yes	Yes
Ky.[2]	....	....	....	....	....
La.	Yes	No	No	Yes	Yes
Maine	Yes	No	Yes	Yes	No
Md.	Yes	Yes	Yes	No	Yes
Mass.	Yes	No[5]	Yes	Yes	Yes
Mich.	Yes	Yes	No	Yes	Yes
Minn.	Yes	Yes	No	Yes	Yes
Miss.	No	No	No	Yes	No
Mo.	Yes	No	No	No	No
Mont.	Yes	Yes	Yes	No	No
Neb.	Yes	No	No	No	Yes
Nev.	Yes	Yes	No	No	No
N. H.	Yes[5]	Yes	Yes	Yes	Yes
N. J.	Yes[5]	No[5]	No	No	No
N. M.	Yes	Yes	Yes	Yes	Yes
N. Y.	Yes	Yes	Yes	Yes	Yes
N. C.	No	No	No	No[5]	No[5]
N. D.	Yes	No	Yes	Yes	No
Ohio	No	No	No[3]	Yes	No
Okla.[2]	....	....	....	....	....
Ore.	Yes	Yes	No	Yes	Yes
Pa.	No	No	No	No	Yes
R. I.	Yes	No[5]	Yes	Yes	Yes
S. C.[2]	....	....	....	....	....
S. D.	No	No	No	No	No
Tenn.[2]	....	....	....	....	....
Texas	Yes	Yes	Yes	Yes	Yes
Utah	Yes	Yes	Yes	No[3]	Yes
Vt.	Yes[5]	No[5]	Yes	Yes	Yes
Va.	Yes	No	No[3]	Yes	Yes
Wash.	Yes	No	Yes	No	No
W. Va.	Yes	No	Yes	Yes	Yes
Wis.	Yes	No[5]	Yes	No	No
Wyo.	Yes	No	Yes	No	No

[1] Compiled from answers to questionnaire sent to Extension Soil Conservationists. In states where there were no Extension Soil Conservationists, questionnaires were sent to the Executive Secretary of the State Committee or to the State Conservationist.
[2] Not reported.
[3] Steps are being taken to inauguarate the described service.
[4] Work up to present "has not been adequate."
[5] Not considered necessary, or no demand for service.
[6] State Soil Conservation "Commission."
[7] State association of district supervisors attempts to supply this or similar service.

TABLE 1 (continued)

SERVICES PROVIDED DISTRICTS BY STATE SOIL CONSERVATION COMMITTEES, 1951 [1]

State	Suggested Plans for Handling Equipment and Other Property	Exchange of Information Among Districts, Via Circular Letter	Guides for Establishing System of Records and Reports	Receives Minutes of All District Boards	Summary of Annual Reports From Districts	Assistance in Obtaining Help From Federal and State Agencies
Ala.	No	Yes	No	Yes	Yes	Yes
Ariz.	No	Yes	Yes	No	No	Yes
Ark.[2]	. . . .	. . . .	. . . .	. . . .	. . . .	. . . .
Calif.	Yes	No[7]	Yes	Yes	No	Yes
Colo.	No	No	Yes	No	Yes	Yes
Conn.	No[3]	No	No[3]	No	No[3]	No[5]
Del.	No	No	Yes	No	Yes	Yes
Fla.	Yes	No	Yes	Yes	Yes	Yes
Ga.	No	Yes	No	Yes	Yes	Yes
Idaho	No	No	No	No	Yes	No
Ill.	Yes	No[3]	No	Yes	No	Yes
Ind.	No	Yes	Yes	No	Yes	Yes
Iowa	Yes	Yes	Yes	No	Yes	Yes
Kan.	No	No[3]	No	Yes	No	No
Ky.[2]	. . . .	. . . .	. . . .	. . . .	. . . .	. . . .
La.	Yes	Yes	Yes	Yes	Yes	Yes
Maine	No	No	No	Yes	No	Yes
Md.	Yes	Yes	No	Yes	No	Yes
Mass.	Yes	No	Yes	Yes	No	Yes
Mich.	No	Yes	Yes	Yes	Yes	Yes
Minn.	No	No[7]	Yes	Yes	No[3]	No
Miss.	No	No[7]	No	No	No	Yes
Mo.	No	No	No	Yes	Yes	Yes
Mont.	Yes	Yes	No	Yes	Yes	Yes
Neb.	No	No	No	Yes	No	No
Nev.	No	No	No	No	No	Yes
N. H.	Yes	No	Yes	Yes	No	Yes
N. J.	No	Yes	No	Yes	Yes	Yes
N. M.	No	Yes	Yes	Yes	No	Yes
N. Y.	No	Yes	Yes	Yes	No[3]	Yes
N. C.	No[5]	No[3]	No	Yes	No	No[3]
N. D.	Yes	Yes	Yes	Yes	No	Yes
Ohio	No	No[3]	Yes	No[3]	No[3]	No[3]
Okla.[2]	. . . .	. . . .	. . . .	. . . .	. . . .	. . . .
Ore.	No	No	Yes	Yes	Yes	Yes
Pa.	Yes	Yes	Yes	No	No	Yes
R. I.	Yes	No	Yes	Yes	No	Yes
S. C.[2]	. . . .	. . . .	. . . .	. . . .	. . . .	. . . .
S. D.	No	No	No	Yes	No	No
Tenn.[2]	. . . .	. . . .	. . . .	. . . .	. . . .	. . . .
Texas	No	No	Yes	No	Yes	Yes
Utah	No	Yes	Yes	Yes	Yes	Yes
Vt.	Yes	Yes	Yes	Yes	Yes	Yes
Va.	Yes	Yes	Yes	No	Yes	Yes
Wash.	No	No	No	No	No	Yes
W. Va.	Yes	Yes	Yes	Yes	Yes	Yes
Wis.	Yes	Yes	Yes	Yes	Yes	Yes
Wyo.	No	No	No	No	Yes	No

[1] Compiled from answers to questionnaire sent to Extension Soil Conservationists. In states where there were no Extension Soil Conservationists, questionnaires were sent to the Executive Secretary of the State Committee or to the State Conservationist.
[2] Not reported.
[3] Steps are being taken to inauguarate the described service.
[4] Work up to present "has not been adequate."
[5] Not considered necessary, or no demand for service.
[6] State Soil Conservation "Commission."
[7] State association of district supervisors attempts to supply this or similar service.

State	Information re Legal Protection in Cases of Property Damage, Injury to Employees, etc.	Works With Technical and Educational Agencies To Provide Literature	Works With State Advisory Committee in Providing "Technical" Guides	Joint Meetings of the District Boards	Arranges With State Authorities for Conservation Education
Ala.	Yes	Yes	No	Yes	No
Ariz.	No	Yes	Yes	Yes	Yes
Ark.[2]	....	....	....	....	....
Calif.	Yes	Yes	No	No[7]	Yes
Colo.	Yes	Yes	Yes	No[7]	Yes
Conn.	No[3]	No	No	No[3]	No
Del.	Yes	No	No	Yes	No
Fla.	No	Yes	No	No	No
Ga.	No	Yes	Yes	Yes	Yes
Idaho	No	Yes	No	No[3]	No
Ill.	Yes	Yes	No	Yes	Yes
Ind.	Yes	No	No	Yes	No
Iowa	Yes	Yes	No	Yes	Yes
Kan.	No	Yes	Yes	Yes	No
Ky.[2]	....	....	....	....	....
La.	Yes	Yes	No	Yes	Yes
Maine	No	No	No	Yes	No
Md.	Yes	Yes	Yes	Yes	Yes
Mass.	Yes	Yes	No	Yes	Yes
Mich.	Yes	Yes	No	Yes	Yes
Minn.	Yes	Yes	No	Yes	Yes
Miss.	No	Yes	Yes	No	No[7]
Mo.	No	No	No	Yes	No
Mont.	Yes	Yes	Yes	No[7]	Yes
Neb.	Yes	Yes	Yes	Yes	Yes
Nev.	No	No	....	No	....
N. H.	Yes	Yes	No	Yes	Yes
N. J.	Yes	Yes	No	Yes	Yes
N. M.	Yes	Yes	Yes	Yes	Yes
N. Y.	Yes	Yes	No	Yes	Yes
N. C.	No	No	No	Yes	No
N. D.	Yes	No	No	No	Yes
Ohio	No[5]	No	No	Yes	No
Okla.[2]	....	....	....	....	....
Ore.	Yes	Yes	Yes	Yes	No
Pa.	No	No	No	Yes	Yes
R. I.	Yes	No	No	Yes	No
S. C.[2]	....	....	....	....	....
S. D.	Yes	No	No	No[7]	No
Tenn.[2]	....	....	....	....	....
Texas	Yes	No	No	Yes	No
Utah	Yes	Yes	No	Yes[7]	No
Vt.	Yes	No	No	Yes	Yes
Va.	Yes	Yes	Yes	Yes	Yes
Wash.	No	Yes	No	Yes	Yes
W. Va.	Yes	Yes	Yes	Yes	Yes
Wis.	Yes	Yes	Yes	Yes	Yes
Wyo.	No	Yes	Yes	Yes	No

[1] Compiled from answers to questionnaire sent to Extension Soil Conservationists. In states where there were no Extension Soil Conservationists, questionnaires were sent to the Executive Secretary of the State Committee or to the State Conservationist.
[2] Not reported.
[3] Steps are being taken to inauguarate the described service.
[4] Work up to present "has not been adequate."
[5] Not considered necessary, or no demand for service.
[6] State Soil Conservation "Commission."
[7] State association of district supervisors attempts to supply this or similar service.

Index

Index